Perfect
Executive
Health

ALL YOU NEED TO GET IT RIGHT FIRST TIME

Other titles in this series:

The Perfect Appraisal by Howard Hudson
Perfect Assertiveness by Jan Ferguson
The Perfect Business Plan by Ron Johnson
Perfect Business Writing by Peter Bartram
The Perfect Career by Max Eggert
Perfect Communications by Andrew Leigh and Michael Maynard
The Perfect Conference by Iain Maitland
The Perfect Consultant by Max Eggert and Elaine van der Zeil
Perfect Counselling by Max Eggert
Perfect Customer Care by Ted Johns
The Perfect CV by Max Eggert
Perfect Decisions by Andrew Leigh
The Perfect Dismissal by John McManus
Perfect Empowerment by Sarah Cook and Steve Macaulay
Perfect Financial Ratios by Terry Gasking
Perfect Freelancing by Sean Marriott and Paula Jacobs
Perfect In-House Training by Colin Jones-Evans
The Perfect Interview by Max Eggert
The Perfect Leader by Andrew Leigh and Michael Maynard
Perfect Marketing by Louella Miles
The Perfect Meeting by David Sharman
The Perfect Negotiation by Gavin Kennedy
Perfect PR by Marie Jennings
Perfect Pensions by Barbara Ellis
Perfect People Skills by Andrew Floyer Acland
Perfect Personal Finance by Marie Jennings
Perfect Presentation by Andrew Leigh and Michael Maynard
Perfect Quality by Bryn Owen
Perfect Recruitment by David Oates and Viv Shackleton
Perfect Relaxation by Elaine van der Zeil
The Perfect Report by Peter Bartram
The Perfect Sale by Nick Thornley and Dan Lees
Perfect Stress Control by Carole McKenzie
Perfect Teamwork by Ron Johnson
Perfect Time Management by Ted Johns

Perfect Executive Health

ALL YOU NEED
TO GET IT RIGHT
FIRST TIME

DR ANDREW MELHUISH

ARROW
BUSINESS BOOKS

First published by
Arrow Books Limited
20 Vauxhall Bridge Road, London SW1V 2SA

Random House Australia (Pty) Limited
16 Dalmore Drive, Scoresby
Victoria 3179, Australia

Random House New Zealand Limited
18 Poland Road, Glenfield
Auckland 10, New Zealand

Random House South Africa (Pty) Limited
Endulini, 5a Jubilee Road, Parktown 2193, South Africa

Papers used by Random House UK Limited are natural, recyclable products made from wood grown in sustainable forests. The manufacturing processes conform to the environmental regulations of the country of origin.

Companies, institutions and other organizations wishing to make bulk purchases of any business books published by Rantom House should contact their local bookstore or Random House Direct:
Special Sales Director
Random House
20 Vauxhall Bridge Road
London SW1V 2SA
Tel: 0171 840 8470 Fax: 0171 828 6681

Random House UK Limited Reg. No. 954009
ISBN 0 09 917582 7

Set in Bembo by
SX Composing Ltd, Rayleigh, Essex
Printed and bound in Great Britain by
Cox & Wyman Ltd, Reading, Berkshire

CONTENTS

PREFACE AND ACKNOWLEDGEMENTS

Having survived the hard work of medical qualification at University College Hospital, London, and the hard play of two years as a ship's surgeon with P&O, I entered general practice as a partner, at Henley-on-Thames in 1965.

Soon afterwards, in 1970, I took over the role of Medical Advisor to Henley Management College where I have been in close contact with business managers and executives for more than 25 years.

My experience at the College encouraged me to research *Executive Health* (Business Books Ltd, 1978). With the expert help of Professor Cary Cooper of UMIST, Manchester, the Henley Executive Research Project was started in 1977. This project has monitored the health of over 500 managers and their spouses through 20 years of dramatic change in society and at the workplace.

After 20 years' full-time general practice and training young general practitioners, I reduced my commitment to the practice to half-time in 1987, job sharing with my GP wife. This left time to supervise the health of senior managers in a number of local companies, and time to write and lecture executives about their health.

I retired from general practice at the end of 1996 but continue with my thriving private and business practice. I plan to continue, as long as possible, my work with companies and executives, together with writing and lecturing.

In the compilation of this book, I acknowledge with thanks the publishers of *Executive Health*, and *Work and Health*

(Penguin Handbooks, 1982); my two earlier books on executives' health.

I also acknowledge *Director* magazine, for which I have been a frequent contributor, together with *International Management* – another regular source of my articles.

This book is written for the executive – male or female – and the text, imitating Churchill, employs the term executive to embrace women managers also.

Many factors affect executive health and the many, often complex, books on the subject vary from 200-600 pages. This book tries to distil the most important facts in a format which the busy executive can read in an hour or two in a plane or train, or on holiday. At the same time it provides a reasonably comprehensive current reference list of further reading and sources of support which are available if more information is needed. One of the great advances of the last 20 years has been the proliferation of well-organized, well-informed self-help groups, and these are well represented.

Last year, at my uncle's funeral, our local vicar preached a short sermon. In six minutes he painted an accurate and well observed picture of my uncle's life. When I thanked him, he commented: 'Any vicar can preach a good sermon for twenty minutes; it takes experience and skill to present one in six minutes.'

David Emanuel, my friend and patient, has helped me to write and edit this book in a similarly disciplined way.

Finally, I would like to thank my committed and forbearing secretary, Jean Dunne, for all her help with this book and with my other work with managers over the years.

SETTING THE SCENE

As we approach the year 2000, the medical understanding of health is that it is determined for all of us by the balance between our natural strengths and weaknesses, and the stress and pressures under which we live.

Our strengths and weaknesses come partly from our genes, partly from the way we live. In this respect, executives are better equipped for survival than other social classes in Britain. Natural selection would be expected to improve their ability to cope well in the modern world.

The executive's environment is also far more healthy. Money produces better quality of life and better education should produce a more healthy lifestyle. Certainly, anti-biotics and heart surgery have saved many lives. But the outstanding improvement in expectation of life and its quality, which has occurred during the twentieth century, is due far more to improvements in standards of living than to medical advances.

On the other side of the coin for executives are the stresses or pressures which their jobs produce. Their hours are long, their responsibilities are great and they travel a lot. Each executive can produce his or her own list of pressures.

The actual facts, the knowledge we have gained from the gathering of information and the research over the last 50 years, show clearly that executives enjoy much better health than their colleagues in other social classes. They live longer and enjoy a better quality of life.

As in business, however, success must not breed com-placency. Most executives could enjoy much better health. Two areas are particularly important:

HEART DISEASE

Heart disease remains the scourge of executive health. Recent national figures report that 36 per cent of all deaths between the ages of 35 and 65 are caused by heart disease and the executive seems to be particularly at risk, due to a combination of his sedentary lifestyle and the long hours that he works.

The last twenty years have seen dramatic improvements in our knowledge of why heart disease – furring up of the coronary arteries – occurs and ways in which it can be treated. There are few executives – or doctors – who cannot benefit from this knowledge and make changes in their own, and their employees', lifestyles to reduce the risk of this modern killer.

At the same time, we must not lose sight of the fact that the relative importance of the two 'modern killers' – heart disease and cancer – is also due to the fact that fewer younger people now die from malnutrition or infection. Cancers in particular become more common as the body grows older.

EXECUTIVE STRESS

Stress must be one of the most over-used words in modern society. The executive with too much work is said to be under stress; but so is his under-worked colleague – in particular, the redundant manager desperately seeking another job. Many people imagine the executive under constant stress to be thin and anxious, weighed down by responsibility, and with his ulcers gnawing away at his duodenum. Nothing could be further from the truth. Managers are unlikely to develop duodenal ulcers, which occur far more commonly in lorry drivers and clerks.

Stress certainly does exist in modern life and in the modern working environment, but probably no more than in the harder physical environment of nineteenth century Britain. What have changed are the surroundings in which we live and our expectations. Stress can enhance life; it can also harm. Harmful stress is not an inevitable fact of modern working life. It only occurs when the manager fails to manage his life satisfactorily. In this respect, managers have far less excuse if they do suffer stress than the assembly-line workers harnessed inexorably to a boring, repetitive job.

In general, good health, like good money, is earned – not given by right – and executives, nearly all of whom have the ability to alter their working environment, have mostly themselves to blame if they suffer stress at work. They also carry the responsibility of imposing stress on their junior colleagues. Even more important, perhaps, they risk the happiness of their marriage, their partner, their children, their extended family, if they fail to achieve a good balance between work and family.

In Britain today, however, not even the well-organized executive is safe from stress. Jobs are in short supply and the spectre of redundancy lies at the back of most managers' minds. In order to maintain profitability, many firms are demanding far more work from far fewer managers. Some managers may lose their jobs, while those that are secure still have the stressful task of making long-serving, loyal staff redundant.

A further problem may be that the executive faced by redundancy is perhaps more vulnerable than his working-class colleague in similar circumstances, because his lifestyle is based on his good income. He is also often the only wage earner in the home and certainly nearly always the major source of income. So loss of his income would financially cripple the family. With mortgages and school fees unpaid, the family may have to face life in a cheaper house, the children may have to adapt to state education, wives may need to find work, and the whole level of lifestyle throughout the family will be drastically altered.

There is no doubt at all that the majority of executives work under considerable pressure which, at times, can become severe and even intolerable. At the same time, they must remember that not only can they exert a fair amount of control over how and where they work, they nearly all obtain a lot of enjoyment from their work.

The executive can be his own worst enemy. Some years ago, Dr Kenneth Duncan, Occupational Physician at British Steel, wrote: 'Stress is blamed for many of our problems. No word has been more over-used or less understood. It is the OK excuse for failure. Much of what is put down to stress should, more correctly be attributed to affluence, over-indulgence and greed – which drive people on by reckless ambition to seek advancement regardless of job satisfaction and to fight, fair or foul, to keep ahead of colleagues and friends.'

This book is not planned as an exhaustive or learned treatise for medical colleagues or executives with limitless time and interest in their own health and in the health of their colleagues, staff and family. Hopefully, it will provide a stimulating and practical read for busy executives struggling daily to balance work and home, and to cope with a pint of work in a half-pint of time.

If two or three points make sense to the individual executive and prompt him to re-think what he does, and how he lives and works, I will be more than pleased. For those who require more information about specific areas of stress and health, a full reading list is available at the end of the book. There is also a resource list which includes up-to-date details of organizations which can provide help, including specific self-support groups. These have proved invaluable to many of my patients.

2

WHAT IS STRESS: AND DOES IT MATTER?

WHAT IS STRESS?

Stress has always been with us – from BC to PC.

The chemical cocktail that readies Man for physical action had a simple relevance for Ancient Man – faced with the primitive challenge of a human or animal adversary, he utilized the stress reaction to fight or run away. This physical action, in his day-to-day fight for survival, used up his stress chemicals without abiding, negative effects.

Not so for Modern Man or, at any rate, for the company executive battling in a high-tech, competitive business world. In most office situations which set off his stress reaction, he has to cope without fighting or running – so the stress chemicals are not burnt off but linger on. They accumulate over time and produce a range of physical and psychological effects which can threaten both mind and body.

The executive faces more complex pressures than his ancient forebears and his response to challenges is not physical, but emotional. His habitat is sedentary and his response to stress is controlled. He cannot hit his difficult boss or stroppy colleague; nor can he run away. He must smile and cope. But the executive cannot stop his body priming itself for the physical activity it senses as appropriate, and it is the unused products of that priming – the raised blood pressure and pulse, the surge of fats into the bloodstream – that can harm.

If the stress is chronic, if work is frustrating, unhappy and the future uncertain (a reality for many after the turbulence

	Normal (relaxed)	Under pressure	Acute pressure	Chronic pressure (stress)
Brain	Blood supply normal	Blood supply up	Thinks more clearly	Headaches and migraines, tremors and nervous tics
Mood	Happy	Serious	Increased concentration	Anxiety, loss of sense of humour
Saliva	Normal	Reduced	Reduced	Dry mouth, lump in throat
Muscles	Blood supply normal	Blood supply up	Improved performance	Muscular tension and pain
Heart	Normal rate and BP	Increased rate and BP	Improved performance	Hypertension and chest pain
Lungs	Normal respiration	Increased respiration rate	Improved performance	Coughs and asthma
Stomach	Normal blood supply and acid secretion	Reduced blood supply Increased acid secretion	Reduced blood supply reduces digestion	Ulcers due to heartburn and indigestion
Bowels	Normal blood supply and bowel activity	Reduced blood supply Increased bowel activity	Reduced blood supply reduces digestion	Abdominal pain and diarrhoea
Bladder	Normal	Frequent urination	Frequent urination due to increased nervous stimulation	Frequent urination, prostatic symptoms
Sexual organs	(M) Normal (F) Normal periods, etc	(M) Impotence (decreased blood supply) (F) Irregular periods	Decreased blood supply	(M) Impotence (F) Menstrual disorders
Skin	Healthy	Decreased blood supply, dry skin	Decreased blood supply	Dryness and rashes
Biochemistry	Normal: oxygen consumed, glucose and fats liberated	Oxygen consumption up Glucose and fat consumption up	More energy immediately available	Rapid tiredness

Figure 1: effects of pressure on bodily functions

of recession and the process of continuous change in industry and commerce), then the cycle of inappropriate stress response can damage nearly every organ in the body; in particular, the heart.

The specific ills that can flow from unreleased stress are examined later – but how exactly is the stress reaction produced in the body? Figure 1 provides a brief summary of the consequences.

What happens is that the brain assesses a challenge or problem; then, if anxious, responds automatically by stimulating the release of adrenaline and noradrenaline from sympathetic nerves throughout the body.

These chemical mediators have two main effects on the circulation:

- They produce constriction of the small arteries, raising the blood pressure.
- They speed up the heart rate and strengthen its contractions.

Unless the challenge is prolonged, the stress response lasts only a few minutes. It produces increased blood flow to the muscles and brain. This boost mechanism clarifies thought and improves physical performance. The heart and lungs work harder to provide this extra blood. Other systems lose blood. At the same time, glucose and small fat molecules flood into the bloodstream to provide the fuel for action.

This improved physical performance in response to challenge is coupled with a heightened nervous tone mediated through the brain. Executives will be aware of the symptoms of this normal, natural, physical response:

- Increased pulse

- Feeling of sweatiness
- Apprehension
- Hollow feeling in the pit of the stomach brought on by loss of blood
- Looseness of the bowels
- Frequency of passing urine

This is all brought about because the extra blood needed by the muscles to counter the challenge must be diverted away from 'unimportant' organs.

Short bursts of adrenaline enhance the performance of the heart – but the effect of a constant infusion of adrenaline, produced by long periods of stress, is harmful. Initially the heart will just work less effectively; in the long term it will be damaged by this over-activity and the coronary arteries will clog up.

At low to moderate levels of pressure, the stress response works really well, with small increases in pressure resulting in much improved performance. Then, as the levels of stress become higher, the response falls steadily away. Finally, like the machine, comes breakdown.

Whilst too little challenge or stress (boredom) will produce poor performance, too much stress (overload, burnout) will finally destroy. Figure 2 summarizes the situation.

Two important principles are illustrated by this figure. The first is that man behaves like plastic when he is put under intolerable stress, rather than like rubber. However brutal the pressure, removal of the stress allows rubber to resume its previous strength and durability. But this does not apply to plastic – or probably to man. Severe or prolonged stress which takes the plastic beyond its ultimate tensile strength level produces deformation so that when the stress is removed the plastic remains deformed.

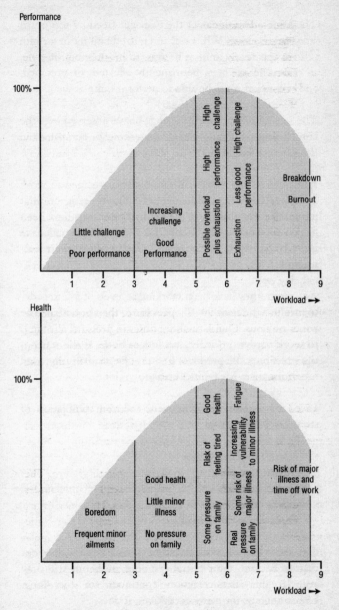

Figure 2: challenge, performance and health

The same effect threatens the manager faced by too much stress for too long. While rest and rehabilitation can see him return, apparently as fit as he was, to his previous lifestyle, in reality he has been permanently affected, or stretched, and will never again be able to perform quite as well.

The second principle is the change I have observed over the last 15 years studying managers working in companies in the south of England.

Fifteen years ago, nearly all the managers seemed to work at a level of 3-5, producing 90-100 per cent of their potential performance. In the last five years they have been forced to work longer hours, take less holiday and have little cover when sickness or holidays affect their colleagues.

As a result, they have been working at levels of 5-7 in order to produce the same 90-100 per cent of their potential. The risk is obvious. Our natural response to greater challenge is to work harder or longer, but longer hours at this stage of the stress response produces poorer – rather than improved – performance. Meantime, breakdown looms close.

Faced by a crisis, the adrenaline-induced stimulation of stress can be beneficial:

- Concentration is high
- Mood is serious
- A difficult task can be completed more quickly and efficiently
- Relaxation is impossible

The short term loss of relaxation – even sleep – does not matter. As with the physical response, problems will only arise if the stress reaction continues for too long. Unfortunately, for many executives, it does.

Adrenaline-induced stimulation seems to become an addiction in just the same way as alcohol or heroin. As many addicts cannot stop gambling, so the executive cannot stop working under intense pressure. If he finishes the job in hand, he will find another to maintain the pressure. He even plans busy holidays, avoiding any hint of relaxation, fearful that such luxury might divert him from his working discipline.

As this pressure continues for long periods, the capabilities of the body are exceeded and impairment of health occurs. Such impairment may be mental – constant arousal of the nervous system producing exhaustion – or physical, from the continued alteration of the natural balance of the circulation.

It is easy to see how the heart can be a prime target for this physical change, both from its role as a pump and from the possibility that the fats released into the bloodstream but not used up by physical action, will form a sludge and so block the arteries supplying the heart.

The other, varied stress-related diseases can also be explained on the basis of the over-use of the physiological response, as can the mental symptoms of anxiety, sleeplessness and depression.

Examples of long-term, or chronic, stress are the fear, frustration and anger which may be produced by an unhappy relationship with the boss or with a difficult client; or the misery of an unsuitable job. Stress also occurs at times of change, uncertainty, and at specific times such as job relocation, promotion and, just as relevant, *failure* to be promoted.

The sedentary nature of an executive's job can make even the natural, healthy physiological response to pressure potentially dangerous, since the response is not used up or sublimated by physical activity. Long journeys commuting to and from work, or as part of the job, combine lack of control and lack of exercise and also add to executives' problems.

An understanding of the ways in which stress can cause impaired health must benefit the executive. If he can recognize stress in himself, he will be *helped* to differentiate between the natural physiological response to pressure and real illness.

The raised pulse and diarrhoea occurring naturally at times of pressure could be interpreted by the executive as evidence of physical disease – so more worry occurs and the symptoms get worse and worse.

Such a vicious circle is only broken by competent medical intervention, which must exclude physical illness and educate the executive to recognize those particular symptoms as his own natural response to stress. Then, in the future, if he again has the symptoms, he can recognize their origin and adjust his lifestyle, rather than worry unnecessarily about illness.

This is the basis of cognitive therapy which is used to treat many 'stressed' managers.

Most senior executives do make the best use of the body's stress 'choke' (as on a car), their performance being stimulated by a short period of stress, after which the choke is switched off as they relax.

But what happens if the choke is not switched off, if you work late or continue to worry about work when you get home? Or if every day is filled with unhappiness, frustration, fear or uncertainty? The answer is chronic stress – the real threat to health and well-being.

Until you acquire stress-coping strategies, the choke will stay on – and you will be at risk.

DOES STRESS MATTER?

None of these considerations has any relevance to the executive unless there is acceptable scientific evidence to support the association between stress and impaired health, and to point to its importance in economic terms. The stakes involved in stress at work are indeed high.

It has been calculated that one in four managers will die before they reach their 65th birthday – the majority from coronary heart disease. Such figures refer only to death; they take no account of those managers forced into early retirement by illness. Even with early retirement, in 1995 only one in five of all workers lived to enjoy retirement.

Even retirement from work does not take away the medical risk of stress. The superannuation department of one large British firm calculated that in 1977 nearly one half of all its managers retiring at 65 failed to reach their 66th birthday. These figures apply just to executives, despite the fact that they enjoy much better health than their staff.

At a staff level, it has been estimated that over the last 20 years in Britain certificates of mental illness increased by nearly 200 per cent for men and 370 per cent for women and that mental illness – mainly, it seems, related to stress – caused three times more time lost from work than did industrial action.

Other research is of interest in that, in addition to relating stress to poor health, it points out areas of managerial behaviour and lifestyle where stress could be anticipated and prevented. Thus Rosenman and Friedman, two cardiologists who worked in San Francisco, observed in

1975 that heart attacks occurred more frequently in managers with a hard-driving, tense, time-conscious, ambitious personality and termed this 'Type A' behaviour pattern. It contrasted with the relaxed easy-going 'Type B' manager.

They enrolled over 3,000 managers in a long-term trial, split them into Types A and B and watched their future cardiac health. At the end of the trial, evidence of heart disease had been observed nearly twice as often in Type A managers.

The authors are now working on ways of helping Type A managers to modify their behaviour in order to see if this will reduce their risk of heart disease. (See reading list.) A more relaxed attitude will, of course, help their staff just as much as it will benefit their own health!

Other research in America attempted to assess the amount of stress in executives' lives as a numerical score. It was considered that change was the main cause of stress and a list of 43 major life events which might affect executives was compiled. Death of a spouse was marked as 100 and the executives were asked to rate other life events in comparison with this one. Figure 3 shows the resulting scores in this large group.

Very similar values were obtained in groups of Japanese and Swedish executives and in members attending Henley Management College.

With this measure of the amount of stress occurring over a given period, the researchers investigated the relationship between stress and illness. Firstly, they looked at the lives of individual executives − taking their life event scores for each period of six months and placing these scores on a graph, on which they also noted the onset of illness. Thus, anyone who moved house (20 points) in

Rank	Life Event	Mean value
1	Death of spouse	100
2	Divorce	73
3	Marital separation	65
4	Jail term	63
5	Death of close family member	63
6	Personal injury or illness	53
7	Marriage	50
8	Fired at work	47
9	Marital reconciliation	45
10	Retirement	45
11	Change in health of family member	44
12	Pregnancy	40
13	Sex difficulties	39
14	Gain of new family member	39
15	Business readjustment	39
16	Change in financial state	38
17	Death of close friend	37
18	Change to different line of work	36
19	Change in number of arguments with spouse	35
20	Mortgage over $100,000 (£60,000 approx.)	31
21	Foreclosure of mortgage or loan	30
22	Change in responsibilities at work	29
23	Son or daughter leaving home	29
24	Trouble with in-laws	29
25	Outstanding personal achievement	28
26	Wife begins or stops work	26
27	Begin or end college studies	26
28	Change in living conditions	25
29	Revision of personal habits	24
30	Trouble with boss	23
31	Change in work hours or conditions	20
32	Change in residence	20
33	Change in college	20
34	Change in recreation	19
35	Change in church activities	19
36	Change in social activities	18
37	Mortgage or loan less than $100,000 (£60,000 approx.)	17
38	Change in sleeping habits	16
39	Change in number of family get-togethers	15
40	Change in eating habits	15
41	Vacation	13
42	Christmas	12
43	Minor violations of the law	11

Figure 3: social readjustment rating scale

January and changed job (36 points) in March, would score 56 points for the first half of the year.

Individual examples showed how illness clustered around periods when the life event scores were high. Such examples are interesting but not scientifically convincing. To add scientific value, the work was extended by rating the severity of illness in a similar way. It was found that there was a positive relationship between scores for stress in one six-month period and scores for the severity of illness in the following six months.

Finally, this research was made prospective by identifying high-risk and low-risk groups of students and sailors (from the number of life event changes they had experienced in the previous six months), and following up their health over the next 12 months. The results were dramatic; the groups predicted to have a high risk did indeed suffer impaired health. In the case of the students playing American football, the incidence of sports injuries was much higher in the high-risk group – illustrating clearly that stress can produce accident-proneness.

Analysis of the individual scores given to the various sources of stress reveals two important concepts.

- **The importance of the family in causing stress.** When the life event changes are split into family/personal, and work/financial areas, it is quite apparent that over half the high-scoring events come from the family.
- **The accumulative nature of stress.** While a major cause of stress does score high, the combination of several small stresses may produce an equally high score. Thus, the not-uncommon combination of change of residence, change of job and change of children's schooling can produce as high a score as the death of a spouse or divorce. This makes sense in

practical terms, for the widow or widower is usually helped by widespread family and social support, while small stresses may not receive support.

3

THE CAUSES AND MANIFESTATIONS OF STRESS

Stress is usually defined as the healthy response of an individual to the wide variety of factors affecting him at that time. The two factors which determine whether the pressures on an executive's life act as a healthy challenge, producing happiness and good health, or as stress, producing unhappiness and the risk of poor health are:

The vulnerability of the executive. Important determinants of vulnerability are the personality of the executive, his lifestyle and support systems. Personality is not easily amenable to change. Lifestyle and support systems are, however, different. It is easy to visualize a situation in which long hours at work, over a period of time, change the executive's pattern of eating, drinking and sleeping, for the worse. At the same time, such long hours can alienate his most important support system – his family – and reduce the time he has available for exercise, another important source of enjoyment and relaxation, and of physical fitness.

The severity and duration of the pressures. In general, executives work well with acute pressure. It is only when they are vulnerable that such pressure can be harmful. It is chronic pressures such as frustration, anger and continuing problems with interpersonal relationships which carry the greatest risk of pushing them beyond their limits and producing stress.

It is easy to produce lists of potential causes of stress in executives. My own research with Professor Cary Cooper, based on managers attending Henley Management College, and working at Mars and ICI Paints in Slough, identified 'relationship with the boss' as a major cause of stress at work.

We also recruited quite a lot of women managers to the research, no easy task at that time (1976-1981), as many women entered management but few seemed to rise to senior positions. If they did succeed, their achievement in filling senior positions came at the expense of the loss of protection against heart disease that their ovarian hormones should have provided. They developed the same lifestyle – and the same risk of illness – as their male colleagues.

GENERAL CAUSES OF STRESS

Rather than provide a list of potential pressures, I would like to cover a number of areas of behaviour which feature regularly as causes of stress in the managers I see when they become ill, or at routine medical checks.

Control

Modern research on stress in managers clearly identifies the manager's feeling of exerting control over his own work pattern as his major protection against stress. Control banishes uncertainty, another major problem. Most of us can cope with a situation we understand, unpleasant as it may be. We cannot cope with a situation which is not clear – and often end up suspecting the very worst.

My own experience of senior managers bears this out. One senior manager (a heavy smoker) experienced angina whenever he flew abroad. His angina increased all the way up the M4 in his car, peaking as he faced the usual backlog of cars trying to enter Heathrow. Safe parking produced a temporary improvement but his unpleasant chest pain did not settle until he was safely booked in and had been handed his boarding card.

This lesson is just as important at work. The executive should feel that he can control his workload; just as important, he should enable his staff to feel that they have some control over the workload he expects from them. The successful manager needs to make those who work for him feel that they have some control – even when they have little!

Control is just as important at home. Most wives will accept difficult problems – such as long working hours, travel abroad for the company at weekends, cancelled evenings out or even relocation – if they feel that they have some input into such decisions or situations. Wives and families are not secretaries; they cannot be told what to do. The successful executive needs every one of his managing skills to maintain a happy home.

Choice

Choice is another problem frequently faced by executives. Given too much choice, it becomes easy to make the wrong decision.

My own career in medicine was straightforward and relatively stress-free. As students and young hospital doctors we worked hours which must have exceeded those worked by busy executives. But we managed happily because we had a secure career structure and no difficult choices.

Not so my 25-year-old son. After a university education he has a lot of choice but no chance of any secure, long-term job. Voltaire wrote many years ago: 'Work abolishes those three great evils, boredom, vice and poverty!' These words remain true in our modern society where unemployment seems accepted as a way of life which neither government nor society are prepared to address.

Patterns and circles

We all have habits and routines, patterns of behaviour – the time we get up, go to bed, when we leave for work or home, when and where we go on holiday, or how we relax. Such habits easily become self-perpetuating circles, positive or negative.

How often have you reviewed your habits? Why do so many men and women managers check their teeth regularly every six months but rarely their general health? It is easy to stay late at the office after 6pm to avoid the evening rush hour. How often have you considered leaving before the rush hour, one or two evenings each week, to balance the late evenings?

Hopefully, this book may highlight one or two areas where you have a pattern of work or lifestyle which could be reviewed. Perhaps also you can allow your partner or family an input!

Time

Over the last ten years during lectures, I have often asked groups of managers to identify their major source of stress. Nearly every group has agreed that their major pressure is time. They feel they are expected to produce good quality work in half the necessary time.

Time problems always seem compounded by interruptions. In order to make uninterrupted time, the manager arrives early at work, leaves late. The result is increasing pressure at home, less time for relaxation.

Any input on effective time management will improve not only the efficiency of the manager, but also his health.

Fit between manager and job

Many managers and many staff carry out jobs which may not suit their skills and which, as a result, they do not enjoy. When they were appointed, they did the job well and so were left to continue with it. Such mis-match is a potential disaster. Jobs must be regularly reviewed. Every penny spent on good selection and regular appraisal and counselling is justified, in my experience, by the health benefits they produce.

A vicious circle

The difference between success and failure in coping with a day's work can be very little. But if work is not completed punctually, a dangerous vicious circle is in place. It is easy to think that the remaining important task can be done tomorrow – but if we are really honest, we know that tomorrow will be just as busy, just as interrupted. By the time the task is faced, it may well have escalated into a major problem. Meanwhile, we are unhappy, aware that we are not coping.

The answer is easy: a desk that is clear at the end of the day and a firm commitment to complete every task as soon as possible. Achieving such perfection is difficult. Managers should beware the cluttered desk and the pile of un-answered mail. Perhaps more important, they should watch their staff's desks for clues that they are falling behind.

MANIFESTATIONS OF STRESS

Two experiences, some years ago, clarified my thoughts about stress on managers, illustrating its risks and benefits.

On the first occasion, I introduced a young lecturer to a group of doctors and sat behind him as he gave a brilliant talk on a difficult subject. Hands behind back, he appeared to the audience relaxed and decisive. However, from where I sat, I could see that while he was talking, his hands and fingers were continually moving. Eventually, he scratched his palms so badly that one started to bleed.

Enhanced adrenaline levels produced his outstanding, apparently relaxed, talk. Only his hands gave the clue to his inner tension. His skin would soon heal, but I wonder what was happening inside him and how his adrenaline levels were affecting the health of his heart and bowel.

My second example was a 63-year-old patient trying to sell his house for the second time. He was looking forward to retirement and moving down to a cottage in Devon. The first time the sale of his Henley house fell through was at the last minute. On the second occasion, five minutes before contracts were due to be exchanged, he picked up the phone – to be told by his solicitor that, again, the sale had fallen through.

He put down the phone and, seconds later, suffered a heart attack. Fortunately, he survived to enjoy his retirement. Of course, the telephone call did not cause his heart attack; the atheroma had probably been laid down over many years. The stress of the telephone call was the last straw; it presumably produced enough spasm in his coronary artery to complete the deadly circle.

In general, stress shows itself as poor physical or mental health, impaired performance, or an increase in bad habits – and a corresponding decrease in good habits. The distinction between these manifestations of stress is often blurred, for poor health can cause poor performance, as does increased alcohol consumption. Knowledge of such manifestations is important as it can enable managers or professional people to recognize stress in their staff and offer help. However, recognition of stress is often difficult, for the onset can be insidious.

PHYSICAL SYMPTOMS OF STRESS
These may be difficult to spot and the person under stress may just appear 'under the weather' or 'not himself'. In my studies among managers resident at Henley Management College, the following physical symptoms, attributable to stress, were reported most frequently:

- Palpitations – an awareness that the heart is beating forcefully, irregularly or quickly.
- Pain and tightness in the chest.
- Indigestion and abdominal distension and wind.
- Colicky abdominal pain and diarrhoea.

- Frequent passing of urine.
- Impotence or lack of libido (sexual drive).
- Alteration of the menstrual pattern in women.
- Tingling feelings in the arms and legs.
- Muscle tension and, often, pain in the neck or low part of the back.
- Persistent headaches, often starting in the neck and extending forward over the head.
- Migraines.
- Skin rashes.
- Feeling a lump in the throat.
- Double vision and difficulty in focusing the eyes.

PHYSICAL EFFECTS OF STRESS

Prolonged increase of blood flow to the brain may produce headaches, migraines, tremors and nervous tics. Anxiety increases and can produce a persistent dry mouth and lack of saliva – often described as 'a feeling of a lump in the throat'.

- Too much blood to the muscles can produce muscular tension, cramp, pain and aches in the lower back.
- Prolonged overaction of the heart may produce palpitations and hypertension.
- Rapid respiration which easily leads to asthma, particularly when associated with emotional stress. Even if bronchospasm does not occur, increased respiration can produce prickling of the hands and feet, dizziness and fainting through its action in blowing off carbon dioxide.
- Lack of blood to the stomach may produce indigestion and duodenal ulcers, while the bowels are particularly sensitive to stress and may react with colic and diarrhoea.
- The frequent passage of urine when we are anxious may be harmful in the long term.
- Lack of blood to the sexual organs can produce impotence in both sexes and menstrual disorders in the female.

- The body may run short of glucose, with the resultant feelings of physical exhaustion.
- The stress response increases fat content in the blood which builds up if not eradicated by physical action. The fats may add to existing fatty and cholesterol deposits inside arteries and, ultimately, cause furring and blockage.

Chronic stress clearly increases the risk of coronary heart disease both by sustaining raised blood pressure and by contributing to damage of the walls of the coronary arteries through the deposition of harmful fats.

Rupture of an artery is obviously a life-threatening condition. The rupture of a vessel in the brain can cause a stroke and possibly confine the previously healthy and active person to a wheelchair. When coupled with a lifestyle factor such as smoking, stress is clearly implicated in heart and chest diseases. It is also implicated in cancer; smoking-related deaths from lung cancer being a particular, yet unnecessary, danger.

The most important causes of death in Britain today are heart disease, cancer and stroke which, together, in that order, account for 66 per cent of all deaths. The risk to executives is demonstrated in figures from the Registrar General, showing that in the 35-64 age range, 36 per cent of all deaths were due to coronaries, 12 per cent to lung cancer and 7 per cent to strokes.

Figures from general practice and hospital casualty departments suggest that around half of all consultations arise from stress, and that one in four managers will die before their 65th birthday – the majority from heart disease.

However, even these figures do not give the whole story, for mental illness may not be diagnosed by a doctor or even recognized as such by the patient under stress.

MENTAL EFFECTS OF STRESS

The first effects of mental stress are usually changes in behaviour, which may occur both in individuals and in groups, evident in absenteeism or poor work performance. It is possible to spot the individual under mild stress by the following changes in behaviour at work:

- Indecision and unreasonable complaints.
- Increased absenteeism and delayed recovery from accidents and illness.
- Accident-proneness and careless driving.
- Poor work, cheating and evasion.

If these early behavioural changes are not helped either by removal of stress or by increased support, they may proceed to mental illness. It is rare for an episode of mental illness not to be preceded by behavioural symptoms.

In personal behaviour and habits the following changes are common:

- Impaired quality and quantity of work achieved.
- Increased smoking.
- Increased consumption of alcohol.
- Increased dependence on drugs, ie tranquillizers and sleeping tablets.
- Overeating or, less commonly, loss of appetite.
- Change in sleep pattern, difficulty in getting to sleep and waking tired.
- Feelings of tiredness and lack of concentration.
- Increased irritability and anxiety.

It is worth remembering that both mental stress and depression typically produce lack of insight into problems – feelings of unworthiness and fear of making an unnecessary nuisance of oneself. This makes it all the more important that family and colleagues at work should point out to the individual under stress the changes in his behaviour and insist that he seek help. As in early alcoholism, well-intentioned help in concealing early stress symptoms by covering up poor performance can, in actual fact, be highly dangerous.

Many workers live much of their lives just below the threshold – not suffering from physical or mental symptoms enough to attract medical or social help, but locked in a pattern of mediocre performance and indifferent health. The net result is a number of unhappy, ill-tempered, ill-at-ease individuals. It is probably true that, as H. D. Thoreau observed 150 years ago, 'the mass of men lead lives of quiet desperation'.

MENTAL ILLNESSES

The most common mental illnesses caused by stress are an anxiety state and depression. Loss of normal sleep pattern may be a warning that mental stress is changing into mental illness. Disturbances may range from the light and unsatisfying sleep of the anxiety state to long periods of sleeplessness with early waking, and the early morning despair of the full depressive illness.

Neurotic illness is defined as abnormal, or inappropriate, reaction to emotional stress or conflict. For example, anxiety to earn enough money to support the family may change, through prolonged stress, into a compulsion to earn more and more.

Finally, there are psychosomatic disorders in which both emotional and physical factors contribute to illness. These include ulcers and irritable bowel syndrome.

Does the pain of a peptic ulcer quite naturally produce anxiety, or is anxiety the trigger for the ulcer? Such questions remain controversial.

4

MANAGING YOUR STRESS

There seems no doubt that during the last ten years the workload on British managers has become greater, their morale poorer. Some statistics from a 1995 survey by Demos, an independent think-tank, identify the pressures that confront the workforce in Britain:

- 44 per cent reported that they arrived home exhausted.
- Many add Saturday to their working week – 60 per cent of men and 45 per cent of women.
- A quarter of managers take work home several times a week.
- 28 per cent of men work more than 48 hours a week.
- 70 per cent of employees working over 40 hours a week want to work less.
- Since the 1950s, time off for stress-related illnesses has soared 500 per cent.
- Full-time workers in Britain have a longer average working week than any other country in the EC.
- Of working men in Britain, one in three works a six to seven day week.
- The average lunch 'hour' lasts just 30 minutes.

This survey underlines what doctors have known for years – that there is a clear link between chronic stress and physical and mental illness; that the number of people succumbing to stress is at record levels and that, even given these stark facts and figures, many executives (and their companies) are not doing nearly enough to protect individual and corporate health.

THE COMPANY ROLE

Management has the responsibility to provide education about stress and facilities to help those suffering from stress. First, though, they may have to be persuaded that such help is needed. Often, sudden illness is the trigger.

In one firm, the deaths of two middle managers from heart attacks within a three-month period precipitated a change in the firm's approach. This happened despite the fact that the problem of stress had been discussed at board level several times during the preceding two years.

The research department of another company took up stress education after two researchers suffered periods of total memory loss brought on by work-related stress.

One potent factor that may impress senior management is the simple realization, backed up by research findings, that failure to manage stress at work has big financial consequences, especially when key people are struck down.

Management may also observe that many of their brighter staff are requesting early retirement or looking for jobs in other, less frantic, companies, while those remaining are refusing promotion or relocation. Such attitudes reflect the greater awareness of many executives about the priorities of their lives. They may not now see the financial rewards of promotion as adequate compensation for the increased pressure and commitment to work.

The most important causes of stress at work remain uncertainty and the manager's feeling that he is not in control. Management must therefore make every effort to avoid these by good planning and communication.

Stress will also be reduced by a management style which puts a premium on quality of work and does not encourage executives to work late or to go home with a full briefcase. One criterion of a successful executive should be the ability to complete work well within the time constraint of the normal working day.

Delegation must be encouraged as an important part of management, remembering the definition of the successful executive as the one who 'delegates all the responsibility, shifts all the blame and appropriates all the credit'!

Management, and doctors advising management, may become involved with the health of an individual manager to the extent that they lose sight of the effect his ill-health may have on those around him. Alcoholism provides a good example. Management, with responsibility to take a company-wide view of health, may sometimes have to sacrifice the individual for the benefit of the group.

Management should also be aware of the need to take into account the views of an executive's spouse and children when significant changes are proposed. Early warning by management of an impending move, and provision of positive help in the new location, will help. So, too, will the cooperation of the executive in telling management, promptly, if he does not wish to move. That way, stressful confrontation can be avoided.

Ways in which companies can positively influence the health of employees include:

General Medical Care
Provision of a full-time company nurse, if warranted by the number of staff. The nurse will not only deal with trivial first aid matters but act as the conduit for action if a medical emergency arises, and coordinate access to a non-staff company doctor where applicable. She will also be a mine of information about the morale and motivation of the workforce as she treats minor stress-related illnesses.

Medical Insurance
Access to free, or subsidised, membership of schemes for diagnosis and treatment offered by private health providers such as BUPA, PPP, Norwich Union. In Britain, medical

care is provided at general practitioner level almost entirely on the NHS. Seeing your GP privately carries few advantages. Similarly, emergency care which is expensive and specialized needs the resources of the NHS. I would recommend that executives always accept such care should it be necessary. But routine specialist, consultant care is quite different. Private care ensures that the executive sees the consultant personally and operations or other treatment can be planned at the executive's convenience.

Company investment in health insurance is usually well worthwhile. It will give the executive ready access to a range of medical back-up without the worry of huge bills. The individual manager feels cared-for and the company gains by his reduced time off work for recurring medical care.

If company policy does not include health insurance, I would advise any manager to invest in insurance, shopping around for the policy which best suits his and his family's needs.

Routine medical checks
Encouragement of staff, particularly the over 40s, to seek regular routine screening. The best system is a straightforward annual check. This will include weight and blood pressure recordings, together with a careful discussion of the executive's lifestyle. Every two to four years, a more thorough medical will include blood screening, together with resting and exercise cardiograms.

For geographically dispersed companies, full checks can be arranged through BUPA. For less senior staff a company nurse has the expertise to carry out straightforward screening and most GPs now undertake a simple annual 'MOT' under the NHS.

The question of confidentiality remains a potential problem

of the company medical. Executives appreciate confidentiality which enables them to be far more honest in areas such as drinking habits, concerns about their job and worrying chest pain. On the other hand, companies paying for the medical may well feel they should receive a helpful summary of the results. A compromise can usually be reached. What matters is that the agreed procedure is clearly understood by patient, company and doctor.

Of course confidentiality is less of an issue if the medical takes place away from the place of work. Many American companies employ specialized services, or an independent physician in the locality, to carry out their medicals.

Eyes and teeth
Urging staff to have annual dental and eye checks. Dental checks must include informed advice on dental hygiene, how the teeth and gums should be cleaned. Most of our teeth, well-maintained, will last as long as we do. It is the dental caries and plaque, together with the recession of the gum margins, which will leave us requiring false teeth in our fifties and sixties.

The eyes are also of vital importance with today's widespread use of PCs. A regular check is a legal requirement for those using a screen for a significant number of hours each week.

Counselling facility
Ensuring that the personnel department includes staff specially trained in work-related counselling. The identity of such staff should be well publicized so that those under stress can make contact easily without 'loss of face'. The manager's anxieties can then be talked through and appropriate action agreed.

Alternatively, a company may offer access to a personal counsellor (one recognized by the British Association for

Counselling). A number of specialist agencies now offer this kind of service to companies.

Fair work policy
Adopting a 'fair work' policy which aims to limit excessive hours, guarantees fair breaks and, when workload is dramatically increased to meet production deadlines, ensures compensatory time off as soon as possible. This requires careful planning and communication, together with regular feedback from staff to monitor the effectiveness of the policy.

Fitness facilities
In the biggest companies, a gym might be provided in-house. Alternatively, many fitness and sports clubs (squash, tennis, etc) offer substantial discounts to corporate members so that the individual cost is less frightening.

Smaller firms should obtain detailed information about local facilities, including leisure centres run by local authorities, and encourage staff to use them by paying a substantial part of the annual subscription.

All companies should aim to provide good spacious showers and changing facilities at work. Staff can then change if they cycle to and from work, and if they take exercise during breaks in the day.

First aid worker
Smaller companies should always nominate members of staff as a focus for first aid and medical advice, and pay for the relevant training. Clear protocols for dealing with medical emergencies such as chest pain or breathlessness should be in place and all staff should be aware of them. Where a number of departments exist, a first aider should be appointed for each, and their details well publicized.

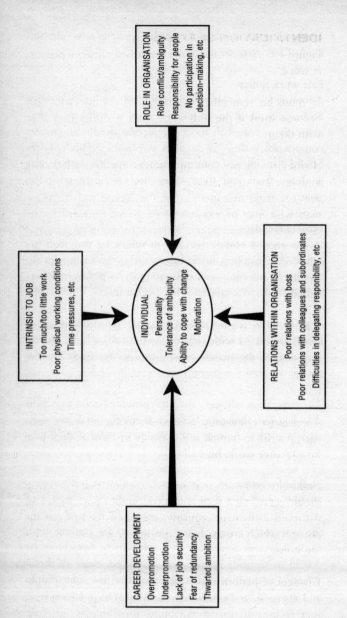

Figure 4: sources of work stress

IDENTIFICATION OF STRESS

Figure 4 identifies some of the important causes of pressure at work.

It must be remembered that the pressures will only become stress if the individual finds it difficult to cope with them.

At-risk jobs. Some jobs themselves are associated with high levels of stress. Examples include the foreman under pressure from management and workers, and the salesman who may be expected to achieve unrealistic sales targets. Rosenman and Friedman in the United States demonstrated clearly the physiological changes occurring in accountants as they approached their annual tax deadlines and the increased illness they suffered at these times.

A change of job is a well known 'at-risk' period, particularly when associated with relocation. Promotion may also be important if the manager is promoted above his level of ability. Regular appraisal and counselling sessions can hopefully identify these victims of the Peter Principle.

The manager's personality. The workaholic, or Type A manager, is a risk to himself and, through his demands on them for excessive work, his staff.

Familiarity with staff. It is most important that executives should get to know their staff as well as they possibly can for if they talk to them regularly, they will then notice the changes which are the best early-warning signs of increasing stress.

Changes of performance will be spotted by regular audit and appraisal, and counselling sessions. Change of behaviour such as increasing irritability, forgetfulness and poor timekeeping, provide early evidence of a stress situation.

Change of habits such as smoking, eating and drinking can only be discovered by careful observation and honest discussion with the individual.

TREATMENT OF STRESS

At a general level, training will encourage early recognition of stress and help individual staff to cope themselves with any early stress situation. Staff can be shown how to increase their resistance to stress through an awareness of the problems and available solutions, both inside and outside the company. Such training is best carried out in groups where it can be taught either as a special subject or as part of a general management course. Either way, this strategy demystifies stress and, with it, the negative notion that a stressed worker is a failed worker.

Companies must have a protocol available for the management of any individual member of staff who suffers acute stress. They require help urgently. Such a protocol must take into account the fact that while outside skilled help may be required, the individual under stress is often best helped within the company by his own boss, by colleagues or by skilled support from the personnel department.

Work in the States in the 1970s showed clearly that the individuals who became anxious or depressed due to stress at work recovered more quickly, and managed better in the future, by staying at work with the help of their supervisor and colleagues. A period away from work takes away the satisfaction which carrying out work produces, along with the support from colleagues, and provides too much time for unhappy thoughts and self-blame.

Sometimes, of course, changes of mood and behaviour due to depression are severe enough to justify a full break from work. In such cases, close liaison between the company and the doctors in charge of rehabilitation is important so that, on return to work, any pressure which has been identified as contributing to the stress can be modified or changed.

Most stress situations will improve if the person under stress is given time to talk, and time to regain confidence. Time to talk must, if possible, be made available at once. Even a few hours of delay can result in the individual's loss of willingness to talk and, so, his capacity to be helped.

Professional counselling often uses a model of the stress situation which distinguishes the factors contributing to stress as follows.

1. *External circumstances* such as promotion at work or family problem.
2. *Internal characteristics* such as Type A behaviour, workaholism and low self-esteem.
3. *Coping mechanisms* such as support from colleagues and friends, relaxation methods, exercise and a healthy eating and drinking pattern.

Cognitive therapy helps the individual to understand what is going wrong, and encourages them to modify their behaviour, alter circumstances and improve coping mechanisms. Specific relaxation techniques can be taught and the stress spiral can be explained and, so, broken.

THE INDIVIDUAL'S ROLE

Coping with stress and protecting your health depends on a good balance between relationships at work and home. It is clear that if an executive's home life is unhappy he will perform less well at work. He will return home late, tired and will soon be even more unhappy. If the situation is reversed – happy at home, unhappy at work – there will still be the vicious circle of stress.

The executive does have a heavier and more time-consuming workload than most of the population. The burden will change throughout his career and he must be constantly aware of the need to achieve the correct balance between work and his outside life.

What then can the executive, beset with conflicting pressures, do to protect himself and his family?

At work
He can strive to limit long hours by better planning and time management, and (hard for many) the ability to say 'no' to extra work that simply can't be managed. He must also delegate more effectively to junior staff.

To achieve these important objectives the executive must learn to be assertive. Indeed, there are training courses to develop such skills. When excessive or unreasonable demands are made, the ability to be assertive – to state your views and position firmly but calmly without losing control and becoming aggressive – is vital, in order to protect your interests professionally and personally. The alternative, aggression, usually produces an uncompromising response, thus creating further stressful conflict and frustration.

Lack of job security and fear of redundancy are major problems, particularly for older executives in a depressed labour market. Such insecurity leads to a fear of delegation to subordinates who are felt by the older manager to be a threat to his position. This then leads to work overload with attendant risks to health and performance, thus making the manager feel even more insecure. The executive who cannot delegate is not doing the job he is paid to do – to organize the work of others.

The skilled executive will make his working life easier by fostering a happy working environment. Letting subordinates participate more in decision-making and the evolution of policy and projects will promote better job satisfaction, curb absenteeism and improve mental and physical health by lowering negative stress levels.

It is important, too, for the executive to limit the needless stress caused by poor planning of journeys, business trips and meetings.

It pays to follow a sensible, balanced diet at work and to watch smoking and drinking levels. Never drink alcohol at lunchtime and don't eat too much lunch. Both destroy the afternoon.

Regular exercise is important too. Even during a busy office day you can stimulate heart and circulation by taking the stairs instead of the lift. A brisk walk at lunchtime will provide good physical exercise and a relaxing break. It seems a pity that it has been left to Japanese firms in Britain to introduce regular exercise breaks during the day. According to research, such breaks certainly improve performance.

At home
The executive's partner can be his best support. In a good relationship, she will be the one he first turns to for advice and support when the going gets tough.

In turn, whatever the work pressures, he must be an equally willing support for her and, between them they must plan, protect and adapt their family and social time to keep a fair balance with the demands of work.

The young unmarried executive easily shares his time between work and social life. But marriage introduces a third segment, time for which has to be found at the expense of either work or social life, or both. Many marital problems arise from this extra demand on the executive's time. It is a difficult, but vital, balance.

Economic considerations and career satisfaction have encouraged more executive wives into a dual role – house-wife and worker. This changing role should create difficulties only if the husband is unwilling to accept it. In return for financial help and a happy wife, he must accept an increased responsibility for looking after the children and running the house – and for the busy executive, this will involve skilful time management and good communications with his spouse. Frankness and honesty in discussion, and a joint agreement to be fair and flexible will greatly reduce the risk of stressful conflict.

If it is appropriate, the reader may give his company marks out of six in the following questionnaire:

1. Provision of regular medical checks.
2. Cars fitted with a company telephone.
3. Provision of exercise facilities where appropriate.
4. Provision of health care insurance.
5. Company health policies for alcoholism, AIDS, etc.
6. Provision of good facilities for eating at lunchtime.

LIFESTYLE IS THE KEY

Most executives enjoy their work and earn enough to maintain a happy home and a comfortable lifestyle. But they are still prone to heart disease and many suffer from stress-related illnesses. Why should this occur? The answer nearly always lies in their lifestyle.

In this chapter, I will cover some aspects of priorities in personal life and, in the next chapter, provide an up-to-date summary of the medical effects of habits on health.

Three medicals I conducted one morning last year clearly illustrated the effects of lifestyle on executive health. The first two were straightforward; both executives took care with what they ate and drank, and took regular exercise. They were pleased to have the chance to demonstrate how well they were. All I needed to do was to reinforce their motivation to maintain what seemed to be a good lifestyle. They worked for a nearby software company which provided annual medical checks, a small gymnasium, shower and changing rooms, and a full-time nurse.

Then came John Lee. All I knew of him was that he lived locally, worked in London and had booked his medical check at his own expense. Thank goodness he did . . . He arrived in a large BMW. He was overweight and looked unfit, but the most striking impression he gave was of tension, like a tightly coiled spring. He sat forward on the front of his chair, talking rapidly, and did not appear to listen. He told me he was 34 – I had guessed that he was 40. This was his lifestyle:

- He left Henley to work in London at 6.30am. He worked steadily through the rest of the day. He returned home some time after 8pm.

- His increasing workload as a City broker meant that he needed to catch up with paperwork at home, in what was left of the evening and at the weekend.
- He saw little of his children, both small. They were usually in bed when he got home and though he hoped to see more of them on holiday, he had only managed two one-week breaks in the last 18 months.
- He had no time for exercise. He had played rugby and rowed at college but excessive workload and time pressure – even on days off – now meant that he took no exercise.
- He smoked 30 cigarettes a day – a habit that had escalated over the years as a way of coping with stress at work, particularly difficult telephone calls.
- He ate poorly – hastily-grabbed sandwiches alternating with generous City lunches.
- He drank alcohol every day. His sandwiches were helped down by a couple of pints of beer, and a half bottle of wine improved his lunch. In the evening, a stiff whisky on his return home helped him to relax.
- He had put on nearly two stones in weight over the last three years.

In addition, he described a poor sleep pattern, headaches and complaints from his wife that he was now rarely interested in sex.

On examination his blood pressure was raised, as were his blood fats. Steady exercise for less than three minutes nearly destroyed him, leaving him coughing and wheezing. His cardiogram after exercise showed early signs of coronary heart disease.

John Lee was not surprised by the results. When I asked him if he was prepared to make changes in his lifestyle he answered 'Yes', revealing that two of his senior partners had recently had heart attacks and, in fact, one had just retired at the age of 44! He added that, to date, of some fifty managers in his firm none had reached the official retirement age of 65 and taken retirement. 'That's why I came to you,' he said. 'Tell me what I should do.'

John Lee, of course, is typical of the hard driving, demanding Type A personality clearly at risk of heart disease in his incessant struggle to achieve more and more, in less and less time. By contrast, the more relaxed Type B personality does not struggle to achieve and so has time to think, weigh odds, to delegate, experiment and be more flexible and creative in his response to challenge. Type A ploughs on, absorbed in making money, meeting deadlines, achieving maximum goals in minimum time.

There is nothing wrong with the positive stress of the workplace. It is the build-up of negative lifestyle traits which disrupt health, work, family. The Type A executive should stand back and review his work environment, his home, his family and his health – and assess how well he is managing them.

After self-appraisal comes goal-setting – and progress needs to be evaluated after, say, three months. For this vital change of behaviour to take root, the executive must enlist the help of work colleagues, friends and, most important, his partner at home.

Here are some suggestions as to how lifestyle could be altered to improve health at home, work and play.

WORKING HOURS

The Government's Social Trends survey shows that the average British father is working a 53-hour week; more, in the case of many executives who are, therefore, in effect absent from the important growing years of their children. The 'reformed' Type A executive could, over time, plan to leave work at work and share more relaxed time at home.

An executive can choose to delegate work more. Assistants and colleagues could assist him to reduce pressure by rescheduling his diary, spacing appointments at longer intervals, allowing realistic times for travel. He might avoid over-commitment by blocking out periods in his diary for 'thinking' or talking to staff. If he finds it hard to curb demands on his time and skill, he could even invest his assistant with the authority to say 'no'!

WORKLOAD/WEEKENDS

A BT survey into the effect of work on home life provides cause for concern and mirrors the dilemma faced by men like John Lee.

- 75 per cent of the managers in the survey reported that work demands reduced to an unacceptable level the amount of time they had at home.
- More than 50 per cent said they had needed to cancel a family holiday or weekend away due to work pressure – a surefire recipe for domestic disaster.
- 65 per cent admitted they had forgotten important dates such as a wedding anniversary or partner's birthday.
- More than 80 per cent said that such behaviour caused rows at home.

Clearly, if this is to change, executives who are behaving in this way must reassess their priorities, devise and assert a healthier working arrangement and, if this cannot be negotiated, contemplate a change of job. The alternative is sombre – disintegration of the family unit and breakdown of health.

FAMILY

However well the executive looks after his body, his health ultimately will be determined by his happiness at work and at home. At work, the fit between his personality and his job control the satisfaction he achieves. His happiness at home will be influenced most by his choice of partner and by their ability to discuss honestly their feelings about having a family.

The more successful the executive is at work, the more time he will want to be there. The happier he is at home, the more he will want to be there. In the end, his happiness and that of his family will depend on his awareness of these conflicts and his ability to resolve them as well as he can.

Type A executive needs to realize that his workaholic ways may deprive him of something worthwhile to work for and a source of enormous pleasure – his family. The best antidote to stress and problems is to talk, and partners are the most effective counsellors. When asked, in my survey at Henley, who helped them the most in times of stress, 80 per cent of executives answered – their spouses.

Just as work needs to be tailored for realistic leisure and family time, so the family scene needs to fit if the balance is to be struck. Company policy and initiatives are the regular products of meetings, so why not adopt the same philosophy at home? Family planning, in the broadest sense, could benefit from a routine regular meeting between husband and wife, with an agenda for discussion – children's needs, family holidays and special days, and so on.

The meeting should be open-ended, lasting as long as is needed so that there are no evasions or misunderstandings. This is necessary for open, honest discussion. A commitment must be made to honour, and implement, decisions and monitor progress. If all this sounds rather formal, remember – at stake is the happiness of the family.

Time management is vital if the manager is to manage his work and family successfully. From many discussions of time management one concept in particular stays in my mind – the first five minutes.

The first five minutes at work can influence the rest of the day. Arrive five minutes early, spend a short time talking with as many staff of all levels as you can, and a good work atmosphere – and a good start to the day – are achieved.

Just as important are the first five minutes at home! That evening, or even a whole weekend, can be ruined by the executive who, arriving home jaded and tired, snaps at his wife, then beats a hasty retreat to his gin or whisky and the evening paper. Just as important is his wife/partner's greeting. A catalogue of disasters during the day, or a complaint about his late or weary arrival, produces a negative atmosphere which can last a long time.

There is little education at school or university about an important challenge of married life; how parents can provide time and love for their children while, at the same time, reserve time and space for each other.

Children can be a blessing – but they can also be a curse! They interfere with the privacy of most married couples for many years. As Francis Bacon wrote in his *Essays*: 'He that hath wife and children, hath given hostages to fortune; for they are impediments to great enterprises, either of virtue, or mischief.'

6

OUR HABITS AND OUR HEALTH

Health in Britain has improved greatly over the second half of the twentieth century – but not as much as might have been expected. The benefits of better diet and living conditions, of antibiotics and improved surgery, have been balanced to some extent by the harmful effects of too much smoking, too much alcohol, too much food. With increased affluence has come the freedom to indulge ourselves as much as we like. Unfortunately, too much can be just as dangerous as too little!

Moderation is not a new concept. It was inscribed on the walls of the temple at Delphi to guide the Greeks, while Buddha admonished his followers: 'Stick to the paths of moderation'.

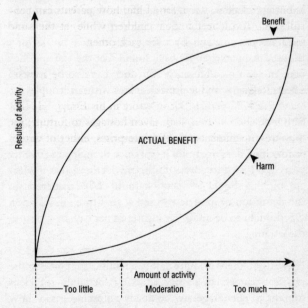

Figure 6: the 'rugby ball'

The concept of moderation comes straight from the stress graph (figure 2, see p.11). For habits, it can be modified to illustrate why moderation works.

Exercise illustrates this graph well. A little exercise may help – but real benefit comes from regular, reasonably strenuous use of the body. Such exercise rarely causes injuries, either immediately or in the future through arthritis or muscle damage. But too much exercise will cause such injuries, influencing future health and breaking the exercise pattern due to the effect of the injury.

It is at the centre of the graph, where the net effect of the activity is maximum. The benefits are high and the risks low. Moderation is nearly always the answer.

An important principle with any habit is what I call the 'Lent effect'. This consists of proving that you control your habits – cigarettes, wine, food – rather than that they control you. All you need to do is stop them for four weeks and see how you manage. By taking caffeine-free breaks for a month, many executives have found that the caffeine they take in tea or coffee each day does have some harmful effects for them, and feel much better without it.

SMOKING

Smoking is unfortunately the one area where the rule of moderation does not hold. It was once thought, and twenty years ago I used to advise during my lectures, that moderate smoking should not be too harmful. What mattered was the definition of moderate – and at that time, moderation was thought to be up to five cigarettes per day, or a cigar in the evening.

Nowadays, there is quite good scientific support for the physical dangers of passive smoking; certainly sufficient support to encourage any company enforcing – as it now should – a strict no smoking policy.

The current prejudice against smokers in companies does seem backed up by scientific evidence and is certainly supported by my own experience. In one company I look after, only two out of thirty senior managers still smoke. I do not believe it is coincidental that it is those same two managers who have developed both some irregularity of their pulses and early evidence of coronary artery disease in the last five years.

Smoking has its benefits. Emotionally, it stimulates and, at the same time, provides relaxation. Medically, it reduces weight. Unfortunately, there are no other medical recommendations and socially, non-smokers now enjoy travel and eating in restaurants far more in a non-smoking atmosphere.

The risks of smoking are now well known. Most important, they are dose-related. Anyone who cannot stop smoking cigarettes or cigars must try to smoke as few as possible. If you must smoke, do be quite certain that you enjoy every bit of every cigarette you smoke. If you don't – stub it out – or, better still, don't light up! Smoke, if it really does relieve your stress, or if you get great pleasure from each cigarette. Alternatively, if, when you try to stop, your secretary or partner begs you to re-start because you are destroying their lives, you may continue smoking. Medical surveys reveal that nearly all smokers want to stop. (Another survey of women smokers included the question: 'Do you smoke after intercourse?' Apparently the research workers had difficulty categorizing the answer: 'I don't know – I haven't looked'!)

In order to stop smoking, the smoker must want to stop more than he enjoys it. This is not easy. Success in stopping smoking takes careful planning so that motivation can be maintained during the period when smoking is stopped, and afterwards when temptation must be avoided.

Acupuncture, hypnotherapy, aversion therapy can all help. Put your pride on the line. Tell all your family, friends and colleagues when you are going to try. Nicotine in patches, or chewing gum, can help the initial withdrawal symptoms. It was thought that cigars carried less risk than cigarettes and that pipe smoking was reasonably safe. This is not true. What matters is the amount of smoke taken down into the lungs. Pipe smoking was probably safer because so little actual pipe tobacco was smoked. It was the ritual of cleaning, loading and lighting the pipe which provided relaxation and benefit.

For the executive who has stopped smoking before he is 35-40, the good news is that nearly all the damage smoking will have done to his heart and lungs will disappear within about three years. Smoking beyond this age rapidly erodes health. By the time the smoker's cough has started, the damage is irreversible.

ALCOHOL

Alcohol represents total destruction to the executive who becomes addicted to it – who becomes an alcoholic. Not only is he destroyed; so are his family and colleagues – and even those he has never seen may be hurt by his badly controlled car. Despite this, public opinion is more aggressive towards tobacco smoking than towards alcohol. The reason probably lies in the social acceptability of alcohol; the fact that most of us drink moderately and enjoy it.

At a company level, the alcoholic tends to conceal his habit. If he can fool himself that he has no problem, and he usually seems to, it is not surprising that he can fool other people.

Some important points about alcohol and the alcoholic are:

- One in fifteen executives has a real drink problem.
- Women, because of metabolic differences, are at risk above half the level of the suggested maximum alcohol

intake for men.

- What are the recommended safe levels of drinking for men and women? The old guidelines advised 21 units per week for men; 14 for women. A unit is roughly the amount of alcohol in a half pint of beer or cider, a standard glass of wine or sherry, or a single of spirits. At the end of 1995, the Department of Health issued new, higher guidelines of up to 4 units per day for men, 2-3 units per day for women. However, the reason for the increase in units – that light drinking may be healthy for the heart in the over 40s – did not impress most medical experts who stressed that the old guidelines should stay, and that the figures expressed are absolute maximums. They advised that higher figures could encourage heavier, regular drinking.

- Four units of alcohol, taken over 2-3 hours with an average meal, will produce a blood level of approximately 80mgs of alcohol in every 100mls of blood. This is the upper legal level for driving in Britain. Above this level, heavy fines and long periods of disqualification from driving are common.

- Wine is the safest drink. Beer is not usually a concern but does contain a lot of calories. Spirits are dangerous. They are concentrated and, if poured for you, can pack more punch than you expect. Whisky seems to be the most often-used crutch for the stressed executive.

- Increased alcohol consumption is a common symptom of stress. It impairs performance by anaesthetising the brain and by diverting its blood supply. Work suffers, stress increases; another vicious circle is started.

The alcoholic

Companies must have in place a well thought out, practical policy to deal with any member of staff who has an alcohol problem. One major company followed this excellent procedure:

1. Anyone considered to have an alcohol problem stopped

work at once. They were immediately checked by their general practitioner or company doctor.

2. An appropriate regime was commenced to resolve the problem. This could be in-patient or out-patient. In-patient care is expensive – but is covered by most health insurance policies, and certainly this company encouraged these for most of their senior staff.

3. Full salary was maintained while they were receiving treatment.

4. Before returning to work, they were checked by the company doctor. At this time, full discussion identified any aspects of the job which could be modified or changed to remove possible sources of stress. They returned to the same job and the same salary.

5. Any recurrence of their problem was treated by instant dismissal. No further treatment was made available.

This policy is based on the fact that such positive support allows the alcoholic himself to come forward early to admit his problem and seek help. It also allows his colleagues to bring his problem early to the notice of senior staff, so that he can be offered help.

But while such early action may help 25-33 per cent of alcoholics to return successfully to work, fewer than 2 per cent of those who lapse after an attempt to rehabilitate can be successfully treated later.

WEIGHT AND DIET

Many executives are overweight. Common causes are:

- Increasing years. Middle-age spread really happens.
- Pressures on time with a resultant lack of exercise to balance their sedentary lifestyle.
- Periods of stress during which they, as do most of us, put food into their mouths to comfort themselves.
- Entertaining out, air travel and hotel living, all of which encourage excessive eating and drinking.

Excess weight can lead to many disorders. It is implicated in heart trouble, diabetes and degeneration of the joints as you age. There are height/age/sex ratios that determine optimum weight – but the evidence of the eye and the tight beltline is enough. If you are not sure, stand in front of your partner, or a mirror, and jiggle your hips – your stomach will probably move in time!

Some important points about weight and diet are:

- If you need to lose weight, don't be drastic – one pound per week is a sensible target.
- If you know you have a large working lunch ahead, you can easily plan a light supper.
- As a rule, cut down on portions, both at home and at work. Do not feel committed to empty your plate.
- Fats are fattening – so avoid where possible.
- Eat a good mixed diet (bread and potatoes are fine, with plenty of fresh fruit and salads and vegetables).
- Stick to three meals a day and no snacking.
- Avoid fattening beer and go for wine or dry sherry, and cut down on sugar – even in the tonic which goes with the gin.
- Regular exercise is a must and, over a fairly long period, increases the metabolic rate and burns up food, so helping to keep down weight.
- Many managers are helped to lose weight by keeping a graph of their weight, recorded daily on good electronic scales. Initial weight is recorded and a target – say a pound a week – agreed. This is entered on the right of the graph, and a straight line outlines the challenge.

   Initially, the manager maintains his normal diet, exercise and lifestyle. Then, every two weeks, he tries something new – such as cutting down on certain foods or alcohol, or taking more exercise. Progress can be monitored and, as the target is not too drastic, hopefully he can keep below the line. If he can, he should lose a stone in three-and-a-half months, and, even more important, do so in a way which teaches him which factors help, or harm, his weight. Such long-term modification can be maintained; short-term starving rarely is.

- Fish is good for you. If you don't enjoy fish, a cod-liver oil capsule a day will probably help to protect your heart and your joints.
- Meat is less healthy. Cut off any obvious fat – unfortunately some fat lies along the muscle fibres which form most of the meat. Spoil yourself with meat two or three times a week.
- Eat a regular breakfast before going to work, if possible including bran. Bran is most easily available in certain cereals and brown bread. Over the last thirty years bran has been established as a vital part of our diet. It forms the bulk which prevents diarrhoea and constipation, absorbs wind and provides benefit to the bowels. Piles, irritable bowel syndrome, bowel cancer, and even heart disease, benefit from regular bran.

EXERCISE

As it is the sedentary life of the executive which helps to put him at risk for heart disease, it is obvious that exercise must help balance this risk to some extent. It also helps the executive to relax. A busy committed day leaves his head still buzzing with activity when he returns home, which distracts him from enjoying his family and often intrudes into his night's sleep. Exercise breaks this pattern of anxiety and, at the same time, burns up the adrenalin which has accumulated during his busy day. The pattern broken, he can share his time at home happily with his family and sleep well.

There has been no change in the medical profession's encouragement of exercise during the last twenty years.

There has been a change in the exercise which doctors have encouraged. Twenty years ago, committed aerobic exercise was regarded as the only effective way to benefit the heart. The pulse needed to be doubled for at least twenty minutes, three to four times weekly, we were told. More gentle exercise – walking, golf and gardening – was considered useless. This advice has now been modified.

Recent research has shown clearly that a brisk half-hour walk, three times a week, protects the heart just as well as a ten-mile run. What matters most is that exercise should be enjoyable. If it is not, it will not be taken.

Exercise can be split into:

Vigorous athletic exercise. This includes squash, rowing, team sports such as football and cricket. These provide excellent protection for the heart against coronary artery disease, by flushing out the coronary arteries, and wonderful relaxation, often with a very supportive group. But there is a risk of muscle or joint injury.

In general, these sports are ideal up to the age of 40. After that, regular training is necessary to maintain the physical fitness necessary to avoid physical injury. Regular visits to the doctor, physiotherapist, or masseur, should trigger a rethink of what is sensible exercise!

Gentle aerobic exercise. This includes jogging, brisk walking, gardening and golf. They are usually enjoyable, benefit the coronary arteries and rarely injure the joints and muscles. A further great benefit is that they can often be shared with your partner and/or growing family – a happy way of combining two important support systems.

Flexibility exercises. These include workouts, exercise classes and programmes. In groups, these are usually enjoyable – in front of the video, motivation can be lost. They benefit the musculo-skeletal system; joints become more mobile, backs less sore. With an aerobic element, they will also benefit the heart. By themselves, they do not.

Muscle-building exercises. These are usually based in gymnasia. They can be enjoyable, but carry few health benefits and many health risks. They do not exercise the heart and the muscle bulk produced is a potential risk to future health.

Some general points about exercise:

- You can afford to kit yourself out well for your exercise. You must! Good trainers reduce foot and ankle problems; a luminous vest can help to protect the jogger from inconsiderate car drivers.
- Warm up before you exercise.
- If you have not exercised for several years, start gently. It has taken that long to get unfit – it will take many weeks or months to get fit again.
- Climbing stairs quickly or a brisk ten-minute walk at the office or airport are of great value in exercising the heart.
- After any flight of more than 3-4 hours try to take some exercise, a brisk walk or a jog, followed by a swim or shower. Jet lag can be halved or even eliminated in this way. Choose a hotel with a fitness facility and indoor swimming pool, if you can.
- Daily, try to move around the office every hour or two and take a 5-10 minute brisk walk at some stage.
- Try to exercise for 20-30 minutes, three times weekly.
- Ideally, exercise is best taken at the end of a busy day when motivation is at its lowest.
- Swimming, jogging, proper walking (four miles per hour), badminton and tennis are all appropriate vigorous forms of exercise – with the bonus that family members can join in.

What is marvellous about exercise is the improvement it

produces in how the executive looks and feels. Often, I cannot believe the change I see in looks and physical results when I carry out a follow-up medical check.

SEX

How often a couple has sex is obviously up to them, a question of mutual agreement. But there are important questions such as: 'When was it last discussed?' 'Are both partners happy about how things are?'

Executives must be aware that when they work hard and long, they will find it much more difficult to make love well at home. Recent research relates more to faithfulness, but is probably relevant. Two studies, one in Japan and one in France, revealed identical results. Heart attacks during sex were very rare – but twice as common in 'away matches'. It seems you can live a double life – but only for half as long.

My experience from research, and from working with managers in companies and in my practice, is that long-term happiness comes from a stable long-term relationship. Such a relationship must involve bad times as well as good. Rows cannot be avoided but do remember the adage 'never sleep on a quarrel'. Making up with sex as a reward seems the ideal answer.

SLEEP

The managers I see describe very different sleep patterns. Some sleep for five hours, others for eight. Most want to know what is recommended medically.

More is now known about sleep, as most large hospitals are equipped with sleep laboratories. In general, their findings are that the benefit you get from sleep follows the standard stress responsive curve. Most middle-aged men need about six or seven hours' sleep, middle-aged women perhaps an hour more. It seems that what matters most is uninterrupted sleep, and that we need a minimum of four to five hours of uninterrupted sleep to be fully refreshed.

Some points about sleep are:

- We all have an optimum period of sleep and probably know it, even if we cannot achieve it.
- Borrowing from this optimum period is like borrowing from the bank; it is expensive and does not resolve the problem. Cutting back on sleep can be a very important trigger for the vicious circle of stress.
- If sleep is lost, an hour of sleep the following afternoon is a very effective way to restore the lost benefit. It can also be a good investment so that an anticipated late night can be enjoyed fully.
- Even a half-hour sleep after lunch is effective in ensuring that the older executive works well through the rest of the day. I remain amazed at how many successful senior managers fit such a period of rest into their busy day.

CAFFEINE AND SALT

The amount of tea and coffee that we drink, and the amount of salt we take with our food are habits which, like many others, are ingrained into our everyday life. They are important, however, in that they do have a real influence on our health.

Caffeine is a powerful drug in its own right, one of the three drugs we enjoy socially which have a significant effect on our health. It produces less problems than the other two (nicotine in cigarettes and alcohol), but it is still potentially dangerous. It is a powerful stimulant which keeps us alert and active and, as a result, can improve performance. But like any other stimulant, it does so at a price.

- It can interrupt sleep and change mood. Many managers I see do experience sleep problems and benefit by

not taking tea or coffee after 6pm.
* Mood changes caused by caffeine include irritability and anxiety, while physical symptoms include shakiness and tremors.
* Palpitations (awareness of a thudding or rapid pulse) are frequently caused by caffeine. At least half of my patients experiencing palpitations benefit by stopping tea and coffee, or by drinking only decaffeinated coffee.
* To my surprise, a recent report showed that instant coffee contained a significant amount of caffeine – almost as much as filtered coffee. Tea contains less caffeine and is therefore a safer drink.

Anyone wishing to test if caffeine is giving them a harmful lift can use the 'Lent' approach. Stop coffee or tea for a month or use decaffeinated. As a result, they may feel better and with the caffeine out of their system, work just as effectively.

Salt. Again, moderation holds for salt. In small amounts it is a vital ingredient of tasty food. In excess, it can push up blood pressure and so put the heart at risk.

If you have a blood pressure problem or strong family history of raised blood pressure you should not add any extra salt to your food.

ASPIRIN AND CHOLESTEROL

A small dose of aspirin is known to prevent heart attacks. Why, therefore, shouldn't we all take the appropriate dose? Blood levels of cholesterol remain as important as ever in the build up of atheroma (blockage) in the coronary arteries. Why can't doctors agree on how to treat their patients with moderately raised cholesterol levels?

Medicine is full of difficult problems such as these. The sheer amount of research in these two areas is staggering. Its volume doubles every fifteen years. An up-to-date summary is impossible in a book like this as the facts change every six months, so I will attempt just a brief summary of the good and bad aspects of treatment in these two areas.

Aspirin has been around for a long time and is used to treat many problems. Thirty years ago its use in small children fell into disrepute because it was suggested that it might be associated with the development of a rare disease called Rey's Syndrome. Since then, its effect in reducing the platelet count in the blood and so reducing the risk of forming clots has brought it back to the centre of medical research and interest. .

There is no doubt that a small dose of aspirin (a Junior aspirin, 62.5mgs) reduces the risk of developing a heart attack or stroke. At the same time, however, it increases the chance of bleeding, for instance, from a duodenal ulcer. With such a minute dose of aspirin the risk is small – but it is there.

Current medical opinion is unanimous in recommending one-a-day Junior aspirin to anyone with known arterial disease. Angina, a heart attack, however small, funny turns (called transient ischaemic attacks) any stroke or evidence of coronary heart disease on a cardiogram, all require aspirin. That is the easy part. The difficult question is whether a fit 55-year-old executive should be taking aspirin to reduce the risk that he will develop coronary artery disease or suffer a stroke in his sixties or seventies.

My advice to the managers I see is that they should consider regular aspirin if they are at present fit but are significantly overweight, have a family history of heart disease, have a suspect blood pressure, or take no exercise. I would not offer it to anyone with digestive problems.

Cholesterol. The strong association between high levels of cholesterol and heart disease has been known for fifty years. As for aspirin, the question of whether to treat is complex, a balance of benefits and risk.

First, and most important, all executives should have one blood test to establish their cholesterol level. If the level is high, a further fasting test will measure the lipoproteins which can be protective (HDL, high density) or dangerous (LDL, low density). Most will be reassured by what is found.

What is now firmly established is that all those with a cholesterol over 6.5 mmols/l should follow a sensible, low cholesterol diet. They may also be helped by garlic pills – Kwai are a good example – which are easy to take and have little effect on the breath. Onions – preferably raw – may also help. Alcohol should be kept moderate, and any extra pounds of weight should be addressed and removed.

Equally certain now is the advice for those with cholesterol levels over 5.5 who have suffered a heart attack or have definite evidence of being at risk. They all require treatment with one of the 'statins' – modern tablets which significantly reduce cholesterol levels – if the other simpler methods of lowering cholesterol have proved unsuccessful. Anyone with a cholesterol over 7.5 on two or more occasions probably requires similar treatment.

As with aspirin, the treatment of moderately raised cholesterol needs careful thought and discussion. Other risk factors need to be taken into account. If the executive or GP is still uncertain, a consultant opinion can also be sought.

RELAXATION AND HOLIDAYS

Most executives always seem busy. Their work is never finished. The job completed is replaced by the next job. Time to relax is somehow wrong, prompting the thought: What have I forgotten?

The problem of constant activity is that it produces an adrenalin 'fix'. The executive performs all day, aided by a flood of adrenaline. The body gets used to this adrenaline buzz, and in the evening and at weekends feels cheated and flat if it is not present. Sleep is interrupted by adrenaline stimulation and work-related thoughts. Weekends have to include as much activity as possible, while holidays if they can be taken (most Type A managers think of themselves as indispensable) must be challenging and active.

Biologically, this constant, frenetic adrenaline-driven behaviour does not work. The stress graph shows this clearly. Irritability and exhaustion occur – but are often not recognized. The vicious circle of stress is in place – for the manager and, if he is senior, for his unfortunate colleagues and staff.

The answer for the executive is an effective way to relax, to break the pattern of constant activity. The material benefits of relaxation are strongly supported by scientific evidence. Twenty years ago, Benson in his book *The Relaxation Response* described his own relaxation technique, and the medical benefits it conferred. Yoga, autogenics, Transcendental Meditation have all been used in industry during the last twenty years, often with great success.

Such methods work well – but only if the executive is organized and motivated enough to employ them. The busier he is, the more difficult it will seem for him to make time for relaxation. As for exercise, itself a wonderful way to relax, what matters is that relaxation should be enjoyable. A happy home life, religious activity, gardening, are all good forms of relaxation.

Holidays provide good relaxation and a commitment to take holidays is a very good marker that the executive is achieving a good balance at work and home, and is prepared to break the 'adrenalin fix.'

Executives should bear in mind the following:

- In my experience, the heavy commitment and the long hours worked by most executives totally justify their taking their full entitlement of holiday.
- Holidays represent a value judgement by the executive on the importance in his life of work and family. Your partner and children deserve your uninterrupted time for a few weeks each year, to balance the time you spend away. If they do not have this, they will take their own holidays – and the family will start to drift away from you.
- Most executives need two full days at the beginning of their holiday before they can fully relax. They also need one or two days at the end of the holiday to get into the right frame of mind to work again. A week's holiday thus produces only three days of full relaxation, a fortnight produces ten days, and three weeks produces seventeen days. It seems no coincidence that our more healthy colleagues in France and Germany usually take three or four weeks holiday in the summer. Nor is it coincidence that our more adrenaline-prone colleagues in the States still take only two weeks holiday each year and cannot face retirement before 65.

In summary, my experience is that good health is the result of maintaining moderation and a sensible balance in our habits as well as in the balance we achieve between work and home. Achieving such a balance in our habits is tricky and personal but it should be possible to avoid excess without taking away too much pleasure. In the past too much medical advice has been negative, puritanical. W. H. Mencken, the American broadcaster defined puritanism as 'the haunting fear that someone, somewhere, is happy.' Happiness and good health do go together. Most executives would agree with John Mortimer when he wrote 'It is not worth giving up everything you like for the sake of an extra

few days in an old people's home in Weston-super-Mare.'
I certainly do!

There are two important approaches which can help you to
manage your own health:

First. Everyone's health is entirely personal. *You* may thrive
on what destroys your colleagues. To make the most of
your natural attributes you should identify your own
strengths and weaknesses. Most of us know how many
hours of sleep we need; how much we can eat or drink
without being excessive. If an executive has high blood
pressure, a low salt diet will reduce weight and, most likely,
blood pressure. If a screening test shows a high level of
cholesterol or fats in the bloodstream, he would be well
advised to limit intake of dairy products. On the other
hand, if tests show normal blood pressure and normal blood
fat content, there seems no logical reason for a change of
lifestyle.

Second. Preserve your own critical judgement about what is
healthy and don't accept medical opinion as being infallible.
Most doctors' advice provides guidelines, not 'tablets of
stone'. Advice about alcohol and exercise changes nearly
every year. Twenty years ago most doctors recommended
low-residue diet to patients with bowel problems, now
they are unanimously in favour of high-residue fibre. You
should always consider moderation, find out what suits you
and what you enjoy and check that the resultant lifestyle
suits your body by having a full medical. Then stick with it,
no matter what the doctors say!

7

MANAGING DIFFICULT TIMES

There is much more pressure on workers now than there was ten years ago. Firms have had to become more efficient, and it seems they have done so at the expense of the health and quality of life of their staff. The rate of change, fast as it is, seems to be accelerating. Firms cannot pause for six months to draw breath and stabilize; if they do their competitors will be out of sight.

But people do not cope well with change; nor does it necessarily produce the best results long-term. Older executives, in particular, find most change threatening. When recently we appointed a new Practice Manager, the only unanimous advice I received from my colleagues at Henley Management College was: 'Don't appoint anyone over 45. They have lost their flexibility.'

As a result, senior executives in companies become younger and the vital balance of youth and experience at senior management level is changed. The older manager must fight for survival in this rapidly changing environment, or accept that he is having difficulty coping and opt for early retirement with the financial pressures and threat to self-confidence that this produces.

It is quite easy to identify a few important areas which can provide major threats or challenges to the executive. Twenty years ago relocation was a major worry. Retirement was not a problem; it was accepted that it would happen naturally at 60 or 65. Redundancy was a disaster; it was perceived by all the executives I saw as something to be ashamed about – total failure!

Now, relocation occurs less often and seems better managed. Redundancy is common but it is no longer a threat.

It is accepted as a fact of life. A long contract now extends for three years!

This suits the company – but does nothing for the confidence of the worker. This chapter will cover a few of these major issues and provide, hopefully, one or two suggestions as to how the executive can cope with these inexorable changes in his environment and lifestyle, and so help him to *enjoy life more*.

WORK/HOME BALANCE

The longer hours and the pressures produced by needing to work with fewer staff must increase pressure on the work/home balance. I have found that successful executives can easily become the victims of their own success at work. Usually they enjoy their work and, as a result, have no difficulty working long committed hours. The more successful they are, the more they are asked to do. It is the rule in most offices that if a job needs to be done, you ask the busy person.

But there are only a certain number of hours in each day. A high workload, often combined with a long journey to and from work, or travel as part of work, must squeeze the time the executive can make available for his family. This easily sets in motion the negative circle, fuelled by the increasing resentment of his family who see his ever-shorter periods at home as a value judgement of their importance in his life.

RELOCATION

Relocation – moving job and home to a new location – is a good example of a change which may represent a major threat, or a major opportunity. Certainly, most companies and most executives themselves could manage it better.

The company can:

- Provide the maximum notice of the possibility of relocation.

- Provide every possible support for the executive and his family to relocate. An interest-free loan should be made available by the company. Small firms can employ a company, with country-wide resources, specializing in relocation. At the new location, staff must be primed to offer all possible support to the new arrivals.
- Accept that more and more of their bright young managers will see the priorities of work and home more clearly perhaps than the company and will decline the offer of relocation if it is not in the family's best interest.
- If possible, avoid offering relocation to managers whose children are between 11 and 18. These children have most to lose by such a move.

The executive can:

- If relocation is suggested, share the decision at once with his family. One senior manager I saw moved every two years through his children's late teenage years. With each move, he left the oldest of his children, 17 or 18, at the previous location. They decided not to share the next move! The pressure on his wife and his work were very great.
- Better still, pre-empt the offer. One executive I met had already talked to his boss and said that he would not move for the next few years. He told me, 'I accept that this decision may affect my career prospects but at this time my health and happiness, and that of my family, come before promotion. The company was disappointed but accepted my decision.'

JOB INSECURITY

It is easy to provide examples of the results of this current problem – far more difficult to suggest solutions.

Companies must be aware of the harmful effects of job insecurity on their staff and address it wherever possible.

Staff are expensive – but they are the life blood of the company and most staff work best under conditions of healthy challenge, not threatened with dismissal if they do not justify their keep.

What matters is that companies are totally open and honest with their employees. Their job prospects must be discussed and documented when they join the company and reviewed at each appraisal and counselling session – ideally once or twice a year. An honest environment at work will certainly reduce some of the harmful effects of job insecurity.

The individual manager must recognize that his job is not for life – and plan accordingly. Mortgages must be kept realistic – even if the company lending the money produces a seemingly generous offer. The negative equity disasters of the last ten years have made this message very clear.

Job insecurity does encourage the dual career family, and partners should obtain extra qualifications and skills whenever the opportunity arises. What matters again is that the executive should be totally open and honest with his family, and his company, about his work situation and ambitions.

FLEXIBLE WORKING PATTERNS
Promotion, relocation or change of job and company all present opportunities for the executive to redefine home and work and aim for a healthier balance that reduces stress all round. It may then be appropriate to discuss with management a work pattern that would allow him to job share or work part-time. There are clear benefits here in terms of less work pressure, less travelling and more quality time at home with the family.

A growing area, even with very large companies, is home working. BT have led the field in this, with many hundreds of employees operating from home. PCs, fax machines, digital-quality telephone and transmission lines and modems, enabling direct links to company computers around the UK – even overseas – are increasingly available and relatively cheap. Their use and sophistication will of course expand dramatically over the next ten years.

Realistically, few executives will ever negotiate a position where they work entirely from home – but it is feasible to spend, say, half the week working from home. The other half can be spent at head office for important meetings, or on the road meeting clients. Because distance from home or office becomes far less important, an added bonus is that the executive and his family can choose pleasant country locations, away from the stress and hassle of city life.

TRAVEL

Business travel is an integral part of most executives' lives. To live in an attractive environment, they normally travel some distance by car or train to work. Work will usually involve travel to the company's other offices or to visit clients. Overseas travel may also be part of the job.

Travel is inherently unhealthy and wastes valuable time. It must, therefore, be kept to a minimum and be accomplished as comfortably as possible. This must involve choices. In general, the medical advice is that if travelling by train or plane is as quick as by road, always use them. Remember that travel by train can be relaxing and much valuable work – and relaxation – can be achieved during a journey by rail.

The health risks of travel have been extensively studied. Recordings of pulse and blood pressure have been made during four-hour car, plane and train journeys. There is no doubt that more stress, as measured by raised blood pressure and pulse, is produced when driving a car than when travelling by train or plane.

Blood fat levels, implicated in heart disease, soar during a long car journey, particularly if the journey is made under pressure. Tests with small electrocardiographs attached to the chest to monitor the heart, show dramatic changes during driving, particularly when the subject overtakes or is caught in a traffic jam. Even those with previously normal electrocardiograms will show unhealthy patterns at these times. But it is those who have previously suffered coronary heart disease who will show the greatest change.

Here are some general guidelines for travel by road and air.

Travel by car

1. The executive must feel he has some control over the choice of car he drives. It is his second office in which he may spend several hours each day.
2. Before buying a car, executives should sit in it for a long journey before committing themselves to two or three years of driving it. Much backache originates in the car. The flexibility and comfort of car seats varies greatly. An automatic gearbox takes some of the hassle out of city driving or commuting.
3. All cars should be fitted with a mobile phone, with appropriate attachment for hands-off use.
4. Ideally, companies should provide a car and driver for all senior executives. Time at the wheel is wasted time and the senior executive's time is very valuable.
5. Most important, executives should remember that the most common cause of accidents on the road is tiredness, so never drive for more than two hours without a stop.
6. Eat and drink regularly when you drive. Hypoglycaemia lowers concentration.
7. Never drink alcohol and drive. Even one glass of wine significantly affects your reaction time.
8. Plan your journey and leave a little earlier than you need to, so that you have plenty time to reach your appointment.

9. If driving alone, the tape of a good book will help you to stay awake and alert – and happy.

Travel by air

1. The executive should always travel 'executive class' when flying, particularly if the journey is for more than 3-4 hours and crosses time changes. His work and his health demand this extra comfort.
2. Do not drink too much alcohol before take-off and do not combine alcohol with tranquillizers.
3. Take a short walk, if possible, before take-off, to compensate for the period of inactivity to follow.
4. Avoid heavy smoking a day or two before travel and avoid over-eating and drinking on the flight. By drinking, of course, I mean alcohol – tea, iced water or soft drinks in as large a volume as possible will improve health.
5. Wear suitable clothing – casual and comfortable.
6. Plan long distance travel carefully. After travel involving six or more hours of time change, leave a full day to acclimatize before getting down to business.
7. Try to arrive in the evening, so that you can start with a good sleep rather than an exhausting social round.
8. Keep your immunizations up-to-date – you never know when or where you may travel. Do not have injections immediately before travel. You cannot afford to be ill when travelling.
9. Finally, remember that a new injection gives protection against hepatitis A (infectious hepatitis). One injection gives immediate protection and a boost, six months later, will protect for ten years. Infectious hepatitis is a bad illness easily acquired in the Middle and Far East.

RETIREMENT

Another vital area in which the executive can improve lifestyle, and longevity, is the issue of retirement and the obvious benefits of early retirement in preserving health and happiness. Retirement should be the happy reward which the executive has earned by his hard, responsible, committed work. It makes sense, therefore, that it should be started as early as possible so that it can be enjoyed while he is fit for as long as possible. It seems quite understandable that the Spanish translation of retirement is 'jubilacion' – jubilation.

Sensible financial provision for early retirement is a must, with contributions enhanced in the final years leading up to the chosen retirement date. Retirement counselling is widely available, and essential. My own patients, taking early retirement, have been rejuvenated – often throwing away previously necessary tablets and embracing a variety of interests and hobbies. The only loser on occasions has been the partner at home whose life will also need to change and who must be involved in any discussion of impending retirement. If they themselves work full or part-time, should this pattern of work be continued and, if so, for how long? If they are at home they may find it difficult to adjust to another person around the house.

So often, during a medical on retired couples, I hear one of the partners say: 'Marriage is for better and for worse, but not for lunch.' The retired executive must not expect his partner to change her life to accommodate his being at home. Remember, she must continue to feel in control. He must negotiate a daily routine which allows the partner to continue her own lifestyle. As Rabbi Lionel Blue said in one of his broadcasts: 'Love is the ability to let the other person be themselves.'

There are four important points to bear in mind when planning early retirement.

- Try to take a long holiday as soon as possible after retirement.
- If you have a routine medical, plan one shortly before retirement and repeat it twelve months later. This second medical will show how your new lifestyle is

affecting your health and physical fitness. It is my experience that both improve.

- Share important activities with your partner. You should both drive, cook and be fully aware of all the details of the family's finances.
- The decision that an executive will retire must be planned as far ahead as possible. The company will benefit greatly – time for replacement is available and the retiring executive can help his successor into the job. At the same time, most caring companies now make available appropriate advice about the realities of retirement and the help they can provide – through seminars and individual counselling.

Recent statistics show that, in Britain, one worker in five does not live to enjoy retirement. Few 60-year-old managers I see enjoy their work so much that they can afford to gamble with these statistics. They are also gambling with the often large amounts of money they have invested in their pension to ensure a happy retirement, mostly wasted if their retirement is cut short by illness.

8

DISEASES AFFECTING EXECUTIVES

Executives, as members of Social Class 1 are about 40 per cent less likely to die between the ages of 35 and 65 than those in the lowest social class – Social Class 5 – according to a recent health census. But while research and medical experience agree that executives enjoy better health than the general population, they must still expect to encounter illness at some time during their careers. In this chapter, I will try to describe briefly the illnesses most likely to affect executives.

Quite often, major underlying problems may be masked or confused by trivial effects. For example, apparent mild indigestion pains may be just that – or may be the precursor of coronary artery disease.

A doctor's advice must be sought by any reader who notices a change in the normal pattern of physical behaviour, such as bowel action or passing of urine, or if mild symptoms persist.

In general, executives share with other members of Social Class 1 much better habits than the other social classes. The most dramatic change in habits since the 1960s has been in cigarette smoking, with Social Class 1 reducing from about 60 per cent smokers then to as few as 20 per cent today. Over the same period, Social Class 5 smokers actually increased from 60 per cent to 65 per cent. Eating habits and exercise also strongly favour Social Class 1. It is only in terms of alcohol related problems that Social Class 1 fares badly; their risk of alcoholism being significantly higher.

At the turn of the century, more than 90 per cent of men

dying between 35 and 65 were cut down by infection or malnutrition. Today, the most important causes of death in this age group are the two modern killers – heart disease and lung cancer.

Within companies two major studies in the States in the 1960s showed clearly that senior executives enjoyed the best health. Middle management were most at risk with pressures to perform from above while, below, there was resistance at shop floor level.

White collar and blue collar middle management often show the worst health pattern, especially heart disease. As in all the other social classes, women live longer, but usually less well. Life expectation has increased in the West to 74 for men and 80 for women but one recent study of five countries, including England, showed that in terms of disability-free life, men enjoyed good quality life up to 73 and women only to 74.

The important message – that it is the quality, not the quantity of life that matters – was nicely summed up by George Bernard Shaw: 'If you give up everything you like, you can live to be 100, or at any rate it will seem like it.'

What happens when mind or body succumbs to a specific ailment? What are the symptoms and treatments available?

First, the physical illnesses.

HEART
Research has confirmed that a family history of heart disease, the level of blood fats, blood pressure and smoking habits are the four key risk indicators for heart disease. On the other hand, exercise has been shown to protect the heart.

Heart disease is the major medical risk for executives. The gradual silting up of one or more coronary arteries through the accumulation of fatty deposits reduces the heart's efficiency, especially under stress, and can produce:

Angina

Under normal circumstances, up to a 50 per cent loss of blood supply to the heart will not seriously affect its performance – but the additional need for blood brought on by exertion (fast walking, or a game of squash) may cause the heart pain we term angina. This stress is quickly resolved when the exercise ceases; thus angina acts as a 'governor' to prevent actual damage to the heart. Any tight, constricting chest pain brought on by exercise or emotional stress may be the precursor of underlying arterial disease and must be checked at once by a doctor.

An exercise cardiogram will show up changes in the ECG after exertion. If indicated, the well-tried procedure of angiography, which is not too invasive, can be used to confirm that there is arterial blockage.

A tablet of trinitrin, placed under the tongue for rapid absorption, will usually ease the distress of angina by dilating the veins to ease the heart's workload and at the same time confirm the diagnosis.

Heart Attack

This is a sudden, tight chest pain usually associated with shock or collapse. The unlucky individual usually suffers tight, constricting, central chest pain, often radiating to the upper abdomen, neck and throat and arms, particularly the left arm. Such heart pain at rest suggests that the blood supply to the heart has been reduced. Associated shock will make the victim of a heart attack appear pale, anxious and restless.

As a quarter of heart attacks are fatal, swift transfer to hospital is vital as those who survive their initial heart attack are most at risk in the first hour. Anyone with severe and unexpected chest pain must be admitted urgently to a coronary care hospital unit. Provision for such urgent action is now achieved in Britain by the ready availability of highly trained paramedics in superbly equipped ambulances. More important, heart attack deaths have been dramatically reduced in recent years by the use in hospital of powerful enzymes to dissolve the clot which is blocking the coronary artery.

A post-coronary exercise cardiogram is usually carried out some four weeks after the heart attack to see whether there is any residual heart damage. If no significant damage has occurred, a positive rehabilitation regime will be planned and will include as much exercise as can be taken by the heart without distress. If the post-coronary angiogram reveals significant remaining blockage of a coronary artery, either angioplasty or coronary artery bypass surgery will be required.

Finally, with the support of family friends and employer, the survivor of the heart attack must confront the need for lifestyle changes to reduce future risks to health.

CIRCULATION

Strokes occur when atheroma and clot block a vessel in the brain. The same factors that contribute to heart disease apply also to strokes which can run a course from mild, recoverable attacks – affecting, for a time, limb mobility or speech – to fatal, massive rupture of a main blood vessel. For some, strokes may mean irrecoverable damage that limits them to a wheelchair for life.

As with heart disease, preventive medicine is vital to spot and stop the insidious build-up of atheroma, which forms the fatty arterial deposits. One of the keys here is blood pressure – a good early indicator of potential problems which can be quickly and regularly monitored. A blood sample will also be helpful in estimating the level of cholesterol which is also implicated in arterial disease.

Executives often find blood pressure measurements hard to understand. The upper value is the systolic pressure, the highest pressure obtained when the heart contracts to push out blood into the circulation. The usual upper limit of normal is reckoned to be 100 plus your age. The lower reading, the diastolic blood pressure, represents the relaxed pressure in the arteries for the rest of the cycle. It should be 90 or less. Systolic and diastolic pressures are now considered to be equally important in producing cardiovascular risk.

Hypertension

Hypertension, or raised blood pressure, should be treated if it is persistently raised. A number of readings of blood pressure, however, are needed before such a decision is reached as drug therapy has many side effects and is usually for life.

Blood pressure varies during the day and from day to day. No executive should accept medication before his blood pressure has been checked several times. As executives are usually covered by health insurance they should, in my view, insist on having a consultant's opinion before starting treatment for raised blood pressure.

Hypertension is potentially dangerous as it rarely produces symptoms but can, at worst, suddenly cause an arterial rupture anywhere in the body. Mild hypertension is usually treated using four groups of drugs. Diuretics help the kidneys to work more efficiently; betablockers block adrenaline release; calcium antagonists and ace inhibitors both dilate the arteries by altering their metabolism.

Side effects are usually not too bad and one or two tablets a day should provide effective protection against heart attacks and strokes. But, again, the stronger drugs do have more side effects, including male impotence.

Hypotension

Conversely, hypotension (low blood pressure) is usually considered to be a blessing, not a problem. On the Continent, however, it is frequently blamed for tiredness and poor performance. At any one time over a million Germans are being treated with drug therapy for hypotension. British and American doctors consider that such people are more likely stressed, unhappy – or both.

RESPIRATORY

Doctors now see less acute and chronic bronchitis because of the reduction in smoking habits. This is balanced, however, by a marked increase in asthma which is thought to relate to greater atmospheric pollution and has distressing results on both mortality and quality of life.

Asthma

About one per cent of the population suffers from asthma, a distressing and potentially dangerous condition marked by wheezing and breathlessness, caused by reversible narrowing of the bronchi.

Asthma is often brought on by allergy, by infection or by emotional factors. In half the cases it starts in childhood. Pollen, house dust and animal hairs can trigger an attack, but in a large number of cases, emotional factors such as worry and excitement are the key factors.

Most GP surgeries now include asthma clinics but treatment is complicated. Different forms of inhalers control the problem for most sufferers but careful diagnosis and monitoring of the success of treatment is needed.

Quality of life has been improved for many with the growing use of steroid-based inhalers, such as Becotide, on a regular 'maintenance' basis. A battery of drugs and treatments will control acute attacks, but the emphasis is on prevention rather than control, including counselling for underlying emotional problems associated with the disease.

Lung Cancer

It goes without saying that smoking and asthma don't mix and, in the case of lung cancer, a scourge which is the most important cause of death from cancer in males in Britain and the third most common cause of female deaths, smoking is a certain trigger.

Disappointingly, there is no early way to diagnose lung cancer – by the time it is identified in a chest X-ray, treatment has very little influence on the outcome. Lung cancer usually produces a persistent cough which brings up blood-stained sputum or pure blood, breathlessness, loss of weight and appetite, and recurrent chest infections. When possible, treatment is by surgical removal, while radiotherapy can also help.

MUSCULO-SKELETAL

Sore backs and necks are a major cause of loss of time at work, with as many as 50 per cent of managers being affected at some point in their working life by a condition that is often stress-related.

The bad back produces severe pain which is so bad that the sufferer cannot move. If this is the case, he must rest and take effective pain relief. If the back pain is not so severe, the trend in treatment now is to advise that rest produces stiffness and is counter-productive. Patients are therefore encouraged to move as much as possible, helped by anti-inflammatory drugs and pain killers.

Physiotherapists, osteopaths and chiropractors help many back sufferers, and their contribution to care is covered by most health insurance. Much good advice about low back pain and neck pain is included in two excellent books by the New Zealand consultant physiotherapist, Robin

McKenzie, and any executive with such pain should find time to read these carefully.

Low Back Pain

Low back problems usually manifest themselves as a stiff sore back. The normal balance of the vertebrae and the surrounding muscles, tendons and ligaments is disturbed and, as a result, the powerful lumbar muscles go into spasm to splint the back and allow recovery. This usually occurs within 7-10 days and does not usually necessitate time off work.

Much more worrying is the occurrence of sciatic pain – pain radiating down one or both legs. This suggests the possibility of a prolapsed disc. The soft intervertebral discs insulate the spine effectively but can slip out of position and press on the sciatic nerve. Sciatic pain must always be taken seriously and medical advice sought quickly. Occasionally, surgery is required to remove a prolapsed disc.

Physiotherapists are especially helpful for both back complaints and the musculo-skeletal injuries that can result from excessive exercise. Physiotherapy can also help ease the movement of joints afflicted by *arthritis*. This is complemented by anti-inflammatory drugs and, if warranted, by steroid injections to the affected area.

GASTRO-INTESTINAL

Ulcers

The relationship between stress and peptic ulcers is complex but stress is known to produce excess digestive acid which can then irritate the stomach lining, or duodenum, and lead to the formation of an ulcer. A quarter of ulcers form in the stomach (gastric ulcer), the rest in the duodenum (duodenal ulcer).

From the age of 35, one man in ten will develop an ulcer. Thirty years ago many ulcers needed surgical intervention. Now, with the advent of drugs which reduce acid formation in the stomach, surgery is very unusual. Tagamet (cimetidene) and Zantac (ranitidine), and other similar drugs, have totally changed the management of ulcers to everyone's benefit. Cimetidene was introduced in the early 1970s and twenty years later another medical advance has improved the management of duodenal ulcers still further. It is now known that a bacterium, helicobacter, must be present in the duodenum to allow formation of a duodenal ulcer. Simple breath and blood tests can now check if this causal bacterium is present and, if so, it can be eradicated with a combination of antibiotics.

Persistent indigestion in those over 40 must always be checked by a doctor in case it masks early cancer of the stomach.

Heartburn

Heartburn is the most common kind of indigestion in those over 50. It results from food-dissolving acid splashing back from the stomach up into the gullet, producing an unpleasant burning sensation.

Heartburn is usually caused by a hiatus hernia, a weakness in the valve which keeps acid down in the stomach. Nervous indigestion (dyspepsia) is frequently linked to stress and worry, with stomach spasms and unpleasant rumbling and belching. A relaxant may be necessary to ease the painful spasms. Modern powerful acid-reducing tablets such as Losec (omeprazole) are very effective in treating heartburn.

Irritable Bowel Syndrome

Often called 'nervous tummy', this condition produces windiness, pain, often diarrhoea, sometimes constipation. It is often associated with stress but, at the same time, its symptoms will produce stress.

Irritable bowel is difficult to manage with medication. A high bran diet usually helps. When symptoms first occur full medical investigations are usually necessary.

GENITO-URINARY

Kidney stones
Perhaps because they work long hours in warm dry conditions, executives do often seem to develop kidney stones. They can cause excruciating pain in either loin, leading down towards the bladder as the urethra goes into spasm when trying to pass a small stone.

The best way to prevent these painful stones is a high fluid intake, up to eight pints a day. Drinking water at bedtime to keep the fluid moving through the kidneys during the night is also helpful.

Cystitis
Cystitis is a common female problem and is less common in men. Infection in the bladder produces small, frequent attempts to pass urine. Passing the urine produces a scalding pain. Prompt treatment is needed with appropriate antibiotics.

Pyelitis
Pyelitis is a kidney infection and much more worrying than cystitis. It can produce high temperatures and, occasionally, rigors and if not treated correctly long-term damage to the kidneys. It requires prompt diagnosis, medication and monitoring.

Gallstones
Although gallstones are often present in the over-40s, they usually give no trouble. It is not certain why they form; they are more common in women.

SKIN

Skin cancers

Skin cancers are more common as we get older and provide another good reason for executives to take out health insurance, as they can be checked quickly and dealt with by a dermatologist. They are usually not as bad as they sound and rarely spread.

Over-exposure to the sun is, of course, a well-documented trigger for melanomas, the really dangerous skin cancer. These develop in moles. Any mole which becomes bigger, bleeds or goes black must be checked urgently by a doctor.

CANCERS (WOMEN)

The breasts

Mortality from cancer of the breast is still distressingly high. Regular inspection of the breasts, early diagnosis of any suspicious lumps and prompt treatment with specific surgery and radiotherapy are required.

The value of mammography in diagnosing breast cancer early is established but there are widely varying opinions as to how frequently such checks should be performed. Not surprisingly, in America, checks are recommended annually. In Britain, the Forrest report targets 50-65 year-old women and the NHS offers a check every three years. I would recommend two checks every three years for all women from 50-70. On alternate occasions, this will involve a visit to a private screening centre.

The uterus

A third of uterine cancers affect the main body of the uterus. They are more commonly found in older women. All post-menopausal bleeding must be immediately investigated. The usual treatment is surgical removal coupled with radiotherapy.

The cervix

The other two thirds of uterine cancers occur in the cervix or neck of the womb. Regular cervical smear tests, every two or three years, are the key to early diagnosis. The smear identifies pre-cancerous cells. Surgical sampling and removal (colposcopy) of the diseased area usually follows.

The ovaries

Screening for this dangerous cancer is difficult because the ovaries are inaccessible. Ultrasound and blood markers have been introduced during the last 20 years but are not yet economically viable. Early symptoms include abdominal pain, swelling and changes in the menstrual cycle. Treatment is surgical removal associated with radiotherapy and/or chemotherapy.

THE MENOPAUSE

The other big issue for women is the menopause and its effects on well-being and the ageing process.

Eighty per cent of women, usually between 50 and 55, will notice the effect of hormonal changes as periods cease. Symptoms include hot flushes, headaches, night sweats, palpitations and insomnia. None of these are pleasant and, in combination, may significantly affect quality of life.

HRT (hormone replacement therapy) is now well-established. It alleviates distressing symptoms and is medically effective in protecting the heart and preventing osteoporosis, the bone-wasting condition. Provided it is only used for eight to ten years in the first place it seems unlikely to increase the risk of breast cancer.

HRT can be taken as pills, patches and implants and with the more recent formulation of pills, withdrawal bleeds can be avoided. It is a complex issue and female executives can request a consultant opinion if they require more advice.

Women with a family history of breast cancer or a history of deep vein thrombosis should always seek a consultant opinion before starting HRT.

CANCERS (MEN)

For men, changes in the *prostate gland* are a routine sign of ageing, with benign enlargement of the gland common in all male executives through their 60s and 70s.

Routine checks can establish the size of the prostate and there are now blood tests to identify any early cancerous changes. Symptoms of prostate trouble include difficulty in starting the urine stream, a poor stream, dribbling at the end, getting up at night to pass water. Any such change should be checked annually by a doctor.

While surgery to the benignly enlarged prostate has improved, Trans Urethral Prostatectomy is still quite a major operation and should not be undertaken lightly.

Cancer of the prostate presents even greater problems as its natural history is still not well understood. Most men over 80 will have developed some cancerous changes in their prostates, but with no harmful effects. This un-certainty has led to big differences of opinion between British surgeons and their colleagues in the States as to when to operate.

For any prostatic symptoms a consultant opinion must be obtained if there is any concern.

NEUROLOGICAL

Headaches

These are perhaps the single most frequent symptom encountered by GPs, and a bane to most executives at one time or another. Most spring from stress, which causes tension in the muscles at the back of the head. Recurrent headaches should be checked by a doctor and optician. Common painkillers, and a determined effort to relax away the tension will deal with most headaches.

Migraines

These arise from a change in the blood supply of the arteries behind the eyes which sets off a debilitating headache. Such headaches are located usually over one or both eyes, can start with a visual disturbance, and can be associated with nausea and sickness. Stress is thought to be linked, and dietary factors such as cheese, chocolate, eggs, alcohol and fats can induce an attack.

Treatment involves identifying, and eliminating, dietary factors; routine painkillers and, where appropriate, specific medication to counter the arterial changes.

EYES

Regular checks with an optician are vital, especially as middle-aged people become progressively long-sighted and may need corrective glasses.

Glaucoma, which often runs in families, is due to a rise in the internal pressure in the eye and is a major cause of blindness. The most common form of glaucoma can be diagnosed by an optician and controlled by medication or surgery before significant loss of vision occurs.

PSYCHOLOGICAL

Mental illness divides between the *psychotic*, a mental condition occurring independent of personality and circumstance, and *neurotic*, where psychological problems arise as an individual struggles with negatives in his lifestyle and environment and reveals itself by abnormal or inappropriate reactions to emotional conflict and stress.

Psychotic illnesses are, thankfully, outside the range of probability for most executives. Their problems are more likely to arise from neurotic conditions – anxiety, phobias, panic attacks and dependencies.

Most important for executives are the various presentations of depression. Around 35 per cent of mentally ill cases seen by GPs involve depression. Depression carries the risk of suicide as long as the condition remains unrecognized and untreated. It is one of the characteristics of depression that the sufferer is loath to ask for help, so friends and colleagues must be alert and help persuade sufferers to seek help.

Manic depressive illness

This shows itself as intermittent bouts of disturbed behaviour. In the manic phase there can be immense constructive energy; the sufferer works for 24 hours at a time, often to great effect. Much great art, poetry and research has been achieved at such times.

Unfortunately, these periods of mania may present great problems at work and home as they do not fit well into routine life. They are also usually followed by periods of severe and debilitating depression.

Sufferers from manic depression are often helped greatly by regular lithium, which modifies and spaces out their attacks, and by appropriate drugs during the manic or depressive phases.

Endogenous depression

This occurs without apparent cause and is a severe illness causing depressed mood, sleep disturbance and self-blame. There is often a similar family history, with depression coming in attacks lasting perhaps six months at a time. It is the form of depression which carries the highest suicide risk.

Reactive depression

This is due to outside stresses, such as problems at the office, redundancy, bereavement and family worries. It represents about 90 per cent of the cases of depression seen by general practitioners. In general, it does not require any drug treatment. Counselling and support should be all that are required, together with occasional use of a mild tranquillizer, or sleeping tablet, for specific symptoms.

The key component of treatment is personal support – by the GP, close family, colleagues, and personal counsellors if warranted.

Mild antidepressants, which help to lift mood, may be appropriate for endogenous depression, along with rest. These drugs have a sedative effect that helps with sleep. Of particular interest at present, from their wide application and success, are the new SSRI drugs such as Prozac (fluoxetine) and Seroxat (paroxetine). For the most chronically depressed these drugs can produce a remarkable improvement in quality of life. Doctors often feel it is worth trying a course of these drugs, to see if they might help. They have the additional advantage that they rarely cause harm in overdose.

Anxiety state

This may show at work as an inability to relax, over-involvement in work and unwillingness to delegate. Common symptoms are vague fears, palpitations, flushing, inability to concentrate, erratic sleep and daytime tiredness. Again, a supportive regime, allowing full discussion of problems, is essential if the patient is to recover equilibrium.

The sudden debilitating terror of a *panic attack* creates a sense of being taken over and being completely out of control. Repetition may lead to a more isolated life and result in *phobias* such as agoraphobia (fear of public places). Trained therapists may be required to help the patient overcome his fears in small, graduated stages. Such treatment is usually very successful – but it is time consuming.

Dependencies

These, like cigarettes, alcohol and even coffee, can all have a bad effect on health. As they are very much part of the social pattern these habits, if over-indulged, can be hard to break – but there is again a role in talking the problems through to understand why the 'crutch' is needed psychologically.

On the plus side, it must be remembered that 50 per cent of all neurotic symptoms disappear without specific treatment, other than sympathy and support.

9

WHAT'S THE ALTERNATIVE?

Probably the oldest and greatest civilization the world has seen remains active in China. It is perhaps enlightening to consider how medicine is practised in this ancient culture. With their great tradition of wisdom, surely they ought to know something about medical treatment.

On a recent visit to China, my wife visited hospitals and medical centres, both modern and traditional. She returned with the clear impression that Chinese medicine combined the best of both worlds. Acute infections, cancers, coronary artery disease were treated, where financially possible, with standard Western-based drugs and surgery. Most other illnesses, helping patients to cope with the discomforts of self-limiting conditions, such as backache and indigestion, and symptoms such as headache, tiredness and insomnia, are treated by acupuncture and other alternative medicines.

Happily, Western medicine seems to be developing along similar lines. More and more doctors, and patients, now seem to accept that health can benefit just as much from approaches outside conventional medicine as from the pills and potions doctors can prescribe. More education is needed – but even during the last ten years, changes have been dramatic.

Sometimes choice of words is important and this would certainly apply to the description of those forms of treatment lying outside conventional medical care. Twenty-five years ago they were labelled alternative medicine. At the mention of an osteopath's help, my senior partner turned puce and apoplectic. 'A referral would take place,' he said, 'over my dead body.' Alternative medicine was exactly what it said – an alternative to conventional care and patients must be advised and helped not to fall into the hands of unqualified quacks.

The major change probably occurred during the 1980s. Complementary medicine gained its title because it earned it. Professions, such as osteopathy, set up full three-year courses with well regulated qualifications as a final reward. Younger general practitioners welcomed the help that complementary practitioners could give to their patients. The modern team approach to general practice has altered the GP's viewpoint. Their objective has become that their patients should receive appropriate help – and not that they should be the sole providers of that help.

My senior partner would certainly be amazed were he to revisit his Henley surgery. A counsellor has been part of the medical team for fifteen years, while next door to the surgery physiotherapists, osteopaths, acupuncturists, chiropodists, aromatherapists and many others offer help to our patients. Again, unthinkable even ten years ago, a significant amount of such care can be claimed under health insurance.

What nearly all complementary practitioners can give to their patients, or clients, is time and care. Time is a commodity which is in short supply for many general practitioners and care can suffer as a result. The general practitioner's role now should be to counsel rather than to prescribe, to guide their patients either towards the care most appropriate for their condition, or towards a better understanding of the condition, so that patients can cope themselves.

Complementary medicine can be expensive, particularly as it is often open-ended. It is worth obtaining from your therapist a realistic idea of what treatment can be expected to achieve, and how long it will take (For example, in-depth counselling may take many years). This information can then be discussed with your general practitioner who can help you to put the time and money involved into perspective.

Of considerable interest in early 1996 was an overview and meta-analysis of the use of hypericum (St John's Wort) extracts for the treatment of depression. In Germany, it is licensed for use in anxiety, depression and sleep disorders and is used extensively. The trials have so far shown that it works better than placebo (inert control), but we await good comparisons with conventional medical antidepressants, such as Prozac. If it is found to be effective, it will provide an attractive alternative to antidepressants as it is so free of side effects.

Over the next few pages, I will try to paint a brief picture of a number of popular complementary disciplines. More information about individual disciplines can be obtained by fax, phone or letter from them. It should be remembered that complementary medicine can help to treat existing conditions – better still, prevent them by improving the body's natural resistance to environmental factors.

Acupuncture
A Chinese technique dating back over 5,000 years and involving the puncturing of the skin with fine needles at points of the anatomy considered most beneficial to the patient's condition. Finger pressure is used too and the aim is to maintain, and restore, good health by re-balancing energy.

The technique has even been used in the operating theatre to achieve pain-free surgery, with obvious benefit to the level of trauma suffered, and recovery times.

Alexander Technique
This discipline is particularly appropriate to executives who spend most of their time sitting at desks, in cars, planes or

trains, and who suffer from back or neck problems. Practitioners aim to improve muscle tone in very specific ways to help the body into better alignment and to ease tension and pain brought on by back trouble.

Fully trained teachers educate their clients one-to-one; group work is not part of this discipline. The principles can be learned and applied in everyday situations and offer the dedicated patient a route to healthier poise and balance, even better breathing and more effective speaking. The technique teaches you to hold your body in a way which is natural and stress-free, and to move in a poised and unhurried manner. Around 20 one-hour sessions are needed to gain proficiency.

Aromatherapy

Another ancient treatment in which oils and aromatic essences are massaged into skin or used as inhalants. Specific combinations are used for the disorder being treated, after the practitioner has taken a client's case history. Psychosomatic and stress-induced mental and physical disorders are said to benefit, along with skin complaints.

Autogenic Training

A self-help exercise system to combat both physical and mental stress. It was conceived by a German doctor in the 1930s. It combines relaxation techniques and psychological off-loading exercises to help get rid of negative emotions such as anger, anxiety or depression which can lead to ill health and under-performance.

Techniques can be learned individually or in groups. They can be acquired over a training period of around eight weeks, with one two-hour session per week.

In the early 1980s groups of managers at Mars in Slough received such an input in sessions provided in the workplace. The majority found the experience very helpful.

Chiropractic

Another ancient discipline, the term – from the Greek – roughly translates as 'treatment by manipulation'. Soft tissue massage and leverage techniques are used to ease tension and free up specific parts of the anatomy whose degeneration trigger conditions such as low back pain, spinal disc problems. Practitioners believe their work has a beneficial effect on the nervous system and can ease a range of ills such as persistent headaches, indigestion, asthma and the skin disorder, psoriasis.

Cognitive Therapy

Evolved in America, this has been gaining ground in the UK, especially among business clients, as a short-cut system that allows negative behaviour patterns to be changed without delving deep into the psyche. The therapist takes a case history and asks the client which specific issues he/she wishes to work on. Discussion leads to an agreement on changed approaches and these are practised by the client, and refined and adjusted at subsequent sessions.

Counselling

Rogerian, Gestalt, Transactional Analysis and Psychodynamic are among the better known counselling techniques. Many evolve from the United States – with five broad categories covering humanistic, behaviouristic, systemic, analytic and hypnotic.

Whatever the discipline, it is important to read about and discuss the various 'schools' before deciding which to follow – and it is important, too, for both counsellor and client to be confident that they can work together. The broad aim is to create, through discussion and insight, possibilities for positive change in lifestyle and relationship situations that undermine a client's psychological health. Many GP practices now have counsellors either attached to the surgery or available from an approved list. Private health insurers will usually fund this kind of therapy, but you should check specifically.

Herbal Medicine

Herbalism evolved from our primitive forebears who identified specific plants and extracts as being beneficial for a range
of conditions. Indeed, some aspects of the modern pharmacy
mimic these ancient preparations. Roots, leaves, stems and
plant seeds are used in a host of combinations, together with
ointment preparations, to treat a wide range of disorders,
often in combination with conventional medicine.

The herbalist will take a careful case history and will pre-
pare medicine specifically for the individual patient – so
different compounds will be used for the same disorder for
different people.

Homeopathy

A key doctrine of this therapeutic approach, pioneered 200
years ago in Germany, is that what we conventionally
regard as the symptoms of a disease are in fact the product
of the body's resistance mechanism. The objective of treatment is to augment that resistance using remedies that
derive from herbs and minerals. 'Like cures like' is a gov-
erning feature – for example, ear-like leaves might be used
to treat ear conditions. Traditionally, homeopathic practitioners will have trained first in orthodox medicine.

Hypnotherapy

The practitioner induces a trance-like state in the patient –
an altered state of consciousness during which positive mes-
sages can be directed at the subconscious, enabling mind
and body to stimulate the healing process.

Hypnotherapy is much used for pain relief and stress disorders such as raised blood pressure, ulcers and bowel
problems. It is also used to explore the subconscious to
identify, and neutralize, painful experiences that may be the
key to psychological disorders and phobias.

Auto-hypnosis can be learned so that the patient himself

can work on problems, having achieved a calm, relaxed state. The latter, though, should be approached with caution and needs reputable support and guidance.

Kinesiology

Evolved in America, applied kinesiology is the science of using simple, gentle, non-intrusive muscle tests to analyse and assess body function and locate energy imbalances which, if allowed to accumulate, will stimulate pain, stress and disease. Specific tests identify imbalances and the practitioner acts directly on the body, through pressure and manipulation, to correct the imbalance. Courses of nutritional supplements may be advised where deficiencies are identified.

Kinesiology is said to be appropriate for a range of physical and psychological conditions and, normally, a short course of weekly visits – topped up at later intervals if required – is all that is needed.

Massage

A universal technique for promoting general good health, it has a long history in cultures all over the world and forms a central part of many complementary therapies.

Centred on relaxation of soft tissue through the removal of built up tension, it also aims to clear blocked energy channels to maintain optimum physical tone, stimulate the immune system and promote a calmer state – a good combination for the harassed executive. For the sport-inclined, it is also a useful procedure for inducing a supple, relaxed state.

Relaxation

So vital for the busy executive trapped in a pattern of hard, committed work, relaxation can be achieved by methods so diverse that they vary from walking the dog at the end of a day's work, to specific techniques for promoting calmness and a sense of physical and psychological well-being.

A number of GPs have demonstrated a reduction in blood pressure, pulse and even blood cholesterol levels in groups of patients taught to relax. In bio-feedback, for example, clients are taught to use conscious effort to control functions like blood pressure which are not normally under voluntary control.

Even the act of praying can regularly reinforce positive thinking and promote a sense of calm. Whatever the chosen method, constant practice is vital and can easily be achieved in just a few minutes each day, during a quiet time at the office or sitting in a car in a traffic jam.

Meditation

Another large area which, as with specific massage and relaxation therapies, promotes mind/body harmony and well being. It has a long history in many cultures and, since the 1960s, has enjoyed renewed popularity with techniques such as Transcendental Meditation (TM).

In a quiet environment, a mental device is repeated to induce a relaxed state. In TM, the teacher selects a special word, or mantra, for each individual while other techniques employ common names such as Majorca (to suggest sunshine and warmth), or a simple number can be repeated. All this is aimed at clearing the mind of clutter and stray thoughts so that in a calm, altered state of consciousness, anxieties are forgotten, and mind and body can relax completely.

This state can also be used for positive thinking. For example, by lowering anxiety levels through repeated meditations it may be possible to cut back, or eliminate, harmful use of cigarettes, alcohol and drug medication.

TM courses start with a preparatory talk and a short private interview, followed by further group sessions and regular appraisal of progress.

Naturopathy

This holds that disease is the body's response to the build-up of toxic rubbish and that conventional medicine frequently masks symptoms – so that, unless the underlying causes are tackled, problems will recur. Naturopaths advocate dieting and fasting regimes to rid the body of toxins and promote a healthier balance. A case history will be taken first and specific therapies tailored to the individual.

The side effects of fasting, as the body ejects toxins, can include halitosis, diarrhoea, vomiting and headaches – so it is important that there is proper support and advice.

Osteopathy

Another therapy based on the manipulation of joints to ease muscle and ligament tension, especially alignment of the spinal column. Many back sufferers seek this treatment.

Practitioners believe that illness and pain result when the vertebrae are out of alignment – a frequent result of poor posture and hours spent slumped uncomfortably in front of a VDU screen or hunched behind the wheel of a car. By resuming normal positions and mobility, better health can be restored.

Shiatsu

Japanese for 'finger pressure', it stimulates, like acupuncture, the energy meridians of the body to restore optimum performance of the bodily organs which are inducing symptoms of ill-health. It is a technique that can be readily taught as it involves no special equipment or remedies – so a family could all learn the procedures and give Shiatsu to each other.

Yoga

Developed in the East over 6,000 years ago, yoga is

universally known and has many branches, hatha yoga being the most common in the West. Techniques of posture, breathing and meditation are all involved and range from the simple basics of an evening class to very advanced attainment.

Again, mind/body balance is the objective and, through trial and error, the student can evolve techniques to deal with specific ill health – for example, persistent stress headaches. Exercises cover Asanas, or postures; breathing, and meditative exercises that help promote calm. Once trained, regular practice takes only a few minutes a day.

10

CONCLUSION

During the last 25 years I have started and finished nearly every talk I have given on executive health with this quotation from Logan Pearsall Smith: 'There are two things to aim at in life: first to get what you want; and after that to enjoy it. Only the wisest of mankind achieve the second.'

I feel sure that most of my readers have achieved already, or will in due course achieve, much of what they want, a good job, children, a lovely home. I hope that this book will help them to enjoy those achievements. In my experience the most important ingredient of their long term happiness is their ability to achieve a successful balance between the demands of work and family.

What I hope is that, while executives will not easily change their attitudes or their life style, they can perhaps modify them. They could do worse than follow Samuel Becket's advice: 'No matter. Try again. Fail again. Fail better.'

Can you bear in mind the remark 'Life is not a rehearsal'. We all have just one chance. Izaac Walton in his book, The Compleat Angler was right when he wrote 'Look to your health; and if you have it, praise God, and value it next to a good conscience; for health is the second blessing that we mortals are capable of; a blessing that money cannot buy.'

QUESTIONNAIRE

Try this quick questionnaire to indicate how much stress you may be under – both through workload and lifestyle.

I have used it for years as a valuable training and evaluation tool in my dealings, and lectures, with hundreds of managers at all levels. The results have been revealing and disturbing – indicating the remorseless rise in managerial stress levels in a leaner, harder working environment.

For questions 1-20, the more 'yes's you score, the higher your stress exposure; more 'no's to questions 21-30 similarly indicate unhealthy exposure to stress.

The scores from this test must be interpreted with care. What is stress for one person can be an exciting challenge for another. In general, high scores do relate to increased stress and the risk of poor health and performance.

A typical scatter of results from a wide cross-section of managers is included.

If your scoring does raise real concerns, it is important to seek medical advice and to review lifestyle options with work colleagues and, critically, your partner and family.

I can well remember a talk at which there were two managers, close friends. Both were 30, married, no children and were successful senior sales managers. They produced strikingly different questionnaires. One scored 5 – very low – and the other a frighteningly high 27. They illustrated clearly the vital point – it is not the pressures we are under but the way we *manage* them that controls stress.

Drinking habits, and questions 15 and 20, are particularly

important as they explore the balance between family and home. Most important of all is question 30 – is the manager content with his way of life? If he is not, then I believe he is at real risk for chronic stress and could be in trouble.

SELF EXAMINATION CHART

	Yes/No	In the last 3 years	Yes/No	Finally	Yes/No
1. Does your work often extend into the evening?	☐ ☐	11. Have you suffered from backache or severe headaches?	☐ ☐	21. Do you find time for regular physical exercise?	☐ ☐
2. Do you bring work home at the weekends?	☐ ☐	12. Have you used tranquillizers or sleeping pills?	☐ ☐	22. Is your sex-drive as strong as ever?	☐ ☐
3. Do you entertain clients to expense-account meals?	☐ ☐	13. Have you had periods of depression?	☐ ☐	23. Have you had a recent medical check?	☐ ☐
4. Do you smoke?	☐ ☐	14. Have you been worried about your health?	☐ ☐	24. Are you as physically fit as you would like to be?	☐ ☐
5. Do you have at least a couple of drinks a day?	☐ ☐	15. Have you been worried about the amount of time you spend with your family?	☐ ☐	25. Do you find enough time to enjoy your hobbies?	☐ ☐
6. Do you spend a lot of time travelling in your car?	☐ ☐	16. Have you been consistently unhappy with your job?	☐ ☐	26. Do you have ways of helping you relax in times of stress?	☐ ☐
7. Does your work involve travel?	☐ ☐	17. Have you changed your job?	☐ ☐	27. Are you satisfied with your standard of living?	☐ ☐
8. Do you feel you have too much responsibility at work?	☐ ☐	18. Have you had to relocate your family?	☐ ☐	28. Do you get full credit for the work you do?	☐ ☐
9. Would you describe yourself as aggressive and mentally tough?	☐ ☐	19. Have you been worried that you might lose your job?	☐ ☐	29. Do you get as much sleep as you need?	☐ ☐
10. Do you weigh more than you should?	☐ ☐	10. Has your spouse complained about the amount of time you devote to your work?	☐ ☐	30. Are you content with your way of life?	☐ ☐

HOW TO SCORE: Questions 1–20 one point for Yes, Questions 21–30 one point for No.

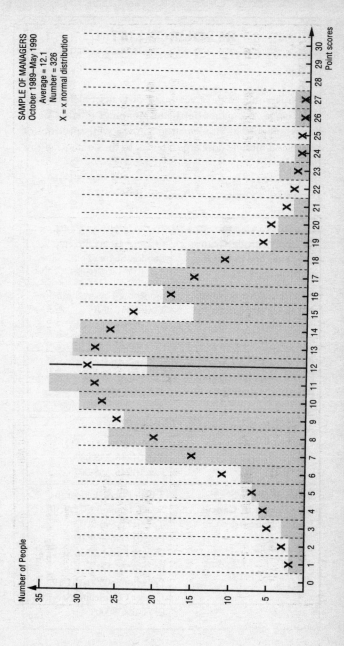

SAMPLE OF MANAGERS
October 1989–May 1990
Average = 12.1
Number = 326
X = x normal distribution

RESOURCE LIST

The following guide gives point-of-contact details for a wide range of organizations and groupings offering treatments, support and information across a wide spectrum of health and lifestyle concerns relevant to the contents of this book.

Details are accurate as at October, 1996.

Al Anon Family Groups (for family and friends of problem drinkers)	61 Great Dover Street, London SE1 4YF Tel: 0171-403 0888
Alcoholics Anonymous (for all UK enquiries)	Stonebow House, Stonebow, York YO1 2NJ Tel: 01904-644 026 Fax: 01904-629 091
Amarant Centre (dealing with menopause issues, including HRT)	80 Lambeth Road, London SE1 7PW Tel: 0171-401 3855 Advice Line: 0891-660 620
Arthritis and Rheumatism Council for Research	PO Box 177, Chesterfield S41 7TQ Tel: 01246-558 033 Fax: 01246-558 007
BACUP (British Association of Cancer United Patients)	3 Bath Place, Rivington Street, London EC2A 3JR Tel: 0171-696 9003 Fax: 0171-696 9002 Cancer Information Service: 0171-613 2121 Freephone: 0800-181 199 Cancer Counselling Service: 0171-696 9000

Better Prostate Healthline	0891-66 77 88
British Acupuncture Association	34 Alderney Street, London SW1V 4EU Tel: 0171-834 1012
British Association for Autogenic Training and Therapy	101 Harley Street, London W1N 1DF Tel: 0171-935 1811 Fax: 0171-224 0478
British Association for Counselling	1 Regent Place, Rugby CV21 2CJ Tel: 01788-550 899 Helpline: 01788-578 328
British Chiropractic Association	29 Whitley Street, Reading RG2 0EG Tel: 0118-975 7557 Fax: 0118-975 7257
British Diabetic Association	10 Queen Anne Street, London W1M 0BD Tel: 0171-323 1531 Fax:0171-637 3644
British Heart Foundation	14 Fitzhardinge Street, London W1H 4DH Tel: 0171-935 0185 Fax: 0171-486 1273
British Homeopathic Association	27a Devonshire Street, London W1N 1RJ Tel: 0171-935 2163
British Naturopathic and Osteopathic Association	Goswell House, 2 Goswell Road, Street BA16 0JG Tel: 01458-840 072 Fax: 01458-840 075
British Association of Psychotherapists	37 Mapesbury Road, London NW2 4HJ Tel: 0181-452 9823

British Society of Hypnotherapists	37 Orbain Road, London SW6 7JZ Tel/fax: 0171-385 1166
British Wheel of Yoga	1 Hamilton Place, Boston Road, Sleaford NG34 7EF Tel/fax: 01529-306 851
BUPA (British United Provident Association)	Thameside House, South Street, Staines TW8 4TL Freephone helpline: 0800-289 577
Cancerlink	11–21 Northdown Street, London N1 9BN Tel: 0171-833 2818 Fax: 0171-833 4963 Helpline: 0171-833 2451
Chartered Society of Physiotherapy	14 Bedford Row, London WC1R 4ED Tel: 0171-242 1941 Fax: 0171-306 6666
Depressives Anonymous	36 Chestnut Avenue, Beverley, East Yorks HU17 9QU Tel: 01482-860 619
Drinkline (largely funded by Dept of Health)	0171-332 0202 (London area) 0345-320 202 elsewhere; info line on freephone: 0500-801 802
Family Planning Association	Margaret Pyke House, 27-35 Mortimer Street, London W1N 7RJ Tel: 0171-636 7866 Fax: 0171-436 3288
Gamblers Anonymous	PO Box 88, London SW10 0EU Tel: 0171-384 3040

General Council and Register of Osteopaths	56 London Street, Reading RG1 4FQ Tel: 0118-957 6585 Fax: 0118-956 6246
Health at Work (for companies and employees)	64 Burgate, Canterbury, Kent CT1 2HJ Tel: 01227-455 564 Fax: 01227-458 741
Health Education Authority	Hamilton House, Mabledon Place, London WC1H 9TZ Tel: 0171-383 3833 Fax: 0171-387 0550 Customer Services Helpline: 01235-465 565
Health Literature Line – for a range of leaflets on health matters, including Health and the Traveller, Women's Health, Mental Health, etc	Freephone: 0800-555 777
Institute of Complementary Medicine	PO Box 194, London SE16 1QZ Tel: 0171-237 5165
International Society of Professional Aromatherapists	82 Ashby Road, Hinckley LE10 1SN Tel: 01455-637 987 Fax: 01455-890 956
Mental Health Helplines **For sufferers from phobias, panic attacks, anorexia and bulimia**	First Steps to Freedom: 01926-851 608
For those suffering anxiety disorders	No Panic: 01952-590 545
For those worried about mental health	Saneline: 0171-724 8000 (London) or 0345-678 000

Migraine Trust	45 Great Ormond Street, London WC1N 3HZ Tel: 0171-278 2676 Fax: 0171-831 5174
National Association for Mental Health (MIND)	Granta House, Stratford Broadway, London E15 4BQ Tel: 0181-519 2122 Fax: 0181-522 1725
National Asthma Campaign	Providence House, Providence Place, London N1 0NT Tel: 0171-226 2260 Fax: 0171-704 0740 Helpline: 0345 010 203
National Council for Psychotherapists and Hypnotherapists	24 Rickmansworth Road, Watford WD1 7HT Tel/fax: 01590-644 913
National Drugs Helpline	Freephone: 0800-776 600
National Health Information Service	Freephone: 0800-665 544
Norwich Union Healthcare	Chilworth House, Templars Way, Eastleigh SO53 3RY Tel: 01703-266 533 Fax: 01703-259 595
PPP (Private Patients Plan)	PPP Healthcare, Phillips House, Crescent Road, Tunbridge Wells TN1 2PL Tel: 01892-512 345 Fax: 01892-515 143 Freephone helpline: 0800-335 555
Pre-retirement Association of Great Britain and Northern Ireland	26 Frederick Sanger Road, Surrey Research Park, Guildford GU2 5YD Tel: 01483-301 170 Fax: 01483-300 981

QUIT (for smokers)	Victory House, 170 Tottenham Court Road, London W1P 0HA Tel: 0171-388 5775 Fax: 0171-388 5995 Freephone Quit Line: 0800-002 200
RELATE (Marriage Guidance Council)	Herbert Gray College, Little Church Street, Rugby CV21 3AP Tel: 01788-573241 Fax: 01788-535007
Royal College of Psychiatrists	17 Belgrave Square, London SW1X 8PG Tel: 0171-235 2351 Fax: 0171-245 1231
Samaritans	10 The Grove, Slough, Berks SL1 1QP Tel: 01753-532 713 Fax: 01753-819 004 Helpline: 0345-90 90 90
SANE (Schizophrenia and National Emergency/ mental health charity)	199-205 Old Marylebone Road, London NW1 5QP Tel: 0171-724 6520 Fax: 0171-724 6502 National Helpline: 0345-678 000
Shiatsu Society	31 Pullman Lane, Godalming, Surrey GU7 1XY Tel/fax: 01483-860 771
SCODA (Standing Conference on Drug Abuse)	Waterbridge House, 32-36 Loman Street, London SE1 0EE Tel: 0171-928 9500 Fax: 0171-928 3343

Society of Homeopaths	2 Artisan Road, Northampton NN1 4HU Tel: 01604–21400 Fax: 01604–22622
Society of Teachers of the Alexander Technique	266 Fulham Road, London SW10 9EL Tel: 0171–351 0828 Fax: 0171–352 1556
Sports Council for England	16 Upper Woburn Place, London WC1H 0QP Tel: 0171–388 1277 Fax: 0171–383 5740
Sports Council for Scotland	Caledonia House, South Gyle, Edinburgh EH12 9DQ Tel: 0131–317 7200 Fax: 0131–317 7202
Sports Council for Northern Ireland	House of Sport, Upper Malone Road, Belfast BT9 5LA Tel: 01232–381 222 Fax: 01232–682 757
Sports Council for Wales	Welsh Institute of Sport, Sophia Gardens, Cardiff CF1 9SW Tel: 01222–397 571 Fax: 01222–222 431
Stroke Association	CHSA House, 123–127 Whitecross Street, London EC1Y 8JJ Tel: 0171–490 7999 Fax: 0171–490 2686
Transcendental Meditation	Freepost, London W1P 4YY Tel: 0171–834 3820 Fax: 0171–630 0924 Helpline: 0990–143 733

UK Council of Psychotherapy	167-169 Great Portland Street, London W1N 5FB Tel: 0171-436 3002 Fax: 0171-436 3013
Weight Watchers (UK)	Kidwells Park House, Kidwells Park Drive, Maidenhead, Berks SL6 8YT Tel: 01628-777 235 Fax: 01628-777 050
Women's National Cancer Control Campaign	Suna House, 128-130 Curtain Road, London EC2A 3AR Tel: 0171-729 4688 Fax: 0171-613 0771

FURTHER READING

Bradford, N, *Men's Health Matters* (Vermilion)
Cooke, Dworkin, *Good Health Guide for Women* (Arrow)
Cooper, C L, *Handbook of Stress, Medicine, and Health* (CRC Press)
Cooper, C L & Straw, A, *Successful Stress Management* (Hodder & Stoughton: British Institute of Management)
Delvin, Dr D, *A-Z of Health & Sex* (Ebury)
Farrell, E, *Mental Health Handbook* (Optima)
Healthy Cooking (Leopard Books)
Healthy Escapes (5th Ed) (Fodor)
McKenzie, Robin, *Treat Your Own Back* (Procare-Medipost Limited)
McKenzie, Robin, *Treat Your Own Neck* (Procare-Medipost Limited)
Marshall, Judi & Cooper, Cary, *Coping with Stress at Work* (Gower Publishing Company Ltd)
Royal Canadian Air Force, *Physical Fitness* (Penguin Books)

PERFECT RELAXATION

Elaine Van Der Zeil

Everyone is talking about stress these days and most people experience its negative symptoms from time to time. What is stress? How does it affect the way we live today? More importantly, how can learning to relax – both physically and mentally – help you to turn your challenges into triumphs?

Perfect Relaxation contains a wealth of strategies to help you take and keep control of your life and your stress levels.

- Understanding what stresses you
- Physical relaxation exercises
- Improving your sleep patterns
- Feeling positive about yourself
- Asserting your needs with others
- Sharing the load
- Managing your time and organizing yourself better
- Switching off
- Questionnaires and personal stress-beating plans

£5.99

ISBN 0–09–970531–1

PERFECT ASSERTIVENESS

Jan Ferguson

Perfect Assertiveness helps you to understand more about assertiveness and its importance as a life skill. The book shows you the difference between assertiveness and aggression, and teaches you to understand more about yourself, the possibilities of change and the potential for improvement in personal, social, family and workplace relationships.

- What does assertiveness really mean?
- Non-assertive behaviour and its results
- What's in it for you?
- You're in charge
- Learn to be your own best friend
- Moving on, letting go
- Handling conflict
- Being an assertive customer
- Setting boundaries and saying 'no'
- Steps to becoming more assertive

£5.99

ISBN 0–09–971051–X

PERFECT COUNSELLING

Max Eggert

This is the ideal book for those who constantly find
themselves in counselling situations at work, at home and
in the office. It will help you to help others.

Perfect Counselling provides you with an overview of what
counselling is (and isn't) and a guide as to when it could
be of value. It is filled with examples and exercises to
guide you through the skills and practice of counselling.

- The process of counselling
- Counselling skills
- When to use counselling and when not to
- Dealing with people who are difficult or reluctant
- Gaining the commitment to action
- Empowerment and taking personal responsibility

£5.99

ISBN 0–09–972881–8

PERFECT EMPOWERMENT

Sarah Cook & Steve Macaulay

Empowerment, one of the most important business concepts of the 1990s, is a technique for improving customer and employee satisfaction. It involves pushing responsibility and authority for decisions affecting the workplace downwards through the organization. Those people closest to the customer are thus enabled to deliver a higher level of customer satisfaction and enhance organizational performance.

Many organizations attempt to empower their employees, but not all are successful. This invaluable book shows how it should be done.

- What is empowerment?
- Planning for empowerment
- Leading the empowerment process
- Creating an empowered environment
- Training and development
- Empowerment through teamwork
- Empowerment in action

£5.99

ISBN 0–09–966981–1

PERFECT DECISIONS

Andrew Leigh

Everybody has to make decisions, and this book gives a
wealth of tips and information on how to make them
more effectively. So much in our lives and careers depends
on taking the right turn when we are faced with a choice
of actions: *Perfect Decisions* helps you to minimize the
guesswork and demystifies the decision making process,
giving you the confidence to weigh up the pros and cons
and pick the best course of action either by yourself or as
part of a group.

- Introduction to decision making
- Problem solving
- The decision process
- Deciding to decide
- Style and intuition
- Tools of the trade
- Group decision making
- Pitfalls, confidence and checklist

£5.99

ISBN 0–7126–5902–1

PERFECT FREELANCING

Sean Marriott & Paula Jacobs

Better communications technology and less rigid working practices allow more people to work freelance than ever before. This creates opportunities for those who: enjoy challenge and variety; need flexible working hours because of family commitments; feel stifled or overlooked in a corporate environment; are facing redundancy but still have much to offer.

Perfect Freelancing takes a practical look at:

* Getting started
* Finding clients – and keeping them
* Coping with the culture shocks
* Working from home and time management
* What to do when things go wrong
* Tax and legal considerations
* Case studies – freelancers and employers compare notes

£5.99

ISBN 0–09–950531–2